PRACTICE MANAGEMENT

A Practical Guide to Starting and Running a Medical Office

Christian Rainer, MD, MPH

PRACTICE MANAGEMENT

A Practical Guide to Starting
and Running a Medical Office

ISBN: 1-55605-365-7

Library of Congress Control Number: 2004103283

WYNDHAM HALL PRESS
Lima, Ohio 45806
www.wyndhamhallpress.com

Printed in The United States of America

Introduction

This book is dedicated to all doctors who are thinking about opening their own shops. It is a big step. Done right, it can open the door to a very satisfying career. Done wrong, it will make you wish you had become a bus driver.

There are many ways to skin a cat. Yet there is not an infinite number of ways. I hope this book will teach you the principles of running a medical practice. Once you have mastered the principles, you can work out the details.

Obviously, not all that has to be learned can be put into a book. When you start on the road to private practice you will likely encounter difficulties that are not mentioned here; either because I was not clever enough to think of them, or because the environment has changed. In any case, a beginner will likely need a little personal assistance. That is what consultants are for. If you have questions or comments, please feel free to contact me at my consulting company, Sunbelt International Consulting, LLC.

website: www.sunbeltinternationalconsulting.com.

Good luck!

Chris Rainer

Table of contents

Chapter 1: CAREER CHOICES

Motto: Why worry about tomorrow, when today is so far away!

You finished residency, now what?

When you enter medical school you know exactly what will happen for the next four years. You also know what will happen after medical school: you will be a resident. The transition between medical school and residency is clear-cut. The residents matching program is well established and enables you to find a suitable residency. However, what happens afterwards is less clear.

You finished residency, now what? Broadly speaking, you have 2 choices:

- You get a salaried job, or
- You open your own private practice.

Salaried jobs

Advantages:

- No need to read this book!
- You will have patients from day one, rather than have to build a practice from scratch. It is safe to assume that any employer who wants to hire a doctor already has enough clients (read: patients) for the new hire. For example, a growing group may have too many patients per physician and may be looking to add a new doctor.
- The usual advantages of any salaried position. Benefits are somebody else's headaches; there is no need to look for personnel, office space, insurance, etc.
- Hospital privileges, if needed, will be provided through employer's channels.
- Cross coverage is assured.

Disadvantages:

- The job will only be as good as the employer. It is difficult to build a satisfactory practice in a chaotic environment over which you

have little control.
- Initially, you will see the patients no other doctor in the group wants for example patients with drug addiction, chronic depression, or simply difficult personalities.
- Little flexibility regarding working hours, dealing with family emergencies (sick children!), scheduling vacations.

1. Private practice

Advantages:

- The most important advantage is that you will have an opportunity to shape your professional life without having to ask your employer for permission.
- Flexibility that extends to many aspects of your life: location, type of patient you want in your practice, type of procedures you do (or prefer not to do), hours of operation, plans to contract with (or to avoid).
- Opportunity to practice as long as you wish since the retirement age is your option.

Disadvantages:

- You need to read this book!
- You have to acquire new knowledge, 1001 things that salaried employees don't need to worry about.
- You are at the mercy of market forces and economic cycles over which you have no influence.
- You will make money if you bother to learn how to run the practice, otherwise not.

Examples of salaried jobs:

- Government jobs, such as VA Hospitals.
- Staff doctor for a large insurer, such as Cigna.
- Joining a group practice.
- Becoming a hospitalist and working for a hospital or a group of hospitalists.

Alternatives to consider:

- Working prn in an ER, urgent care center, cruise ship, doing locums, etc., until you figure out what you want in life.
- Joining the armed forces.

- Enter the academic world, for example as a faculty member at University of Arizona.

Alternative alternatives (things nobody thinks about)

- House calls: don't laugh, but I think this is an excellent opportunity. For example, you can chose a compact, middle class neighborhood and advertise to all households there.
- Hotel doctor: make a deal with the major resorts in your area to put your business card in all rooms, something along the lines of "Feeling sick, call Dr. Flick".

What is likely to happen to you?

So far I discussed some possible career choices. But what is **likely** to happen to you? What does life experience show? My prediction is that **the vast majority of doctors will eventually wind up in private practice.** How soon depends on circumstances. The most likely scenario is a short career as a salaried doctor, followed by the opening of your own practice in the same community within 2-3 years of completion of residency.

Some residents find it difficult to believe that having their own office is a true career option. They regard private practice as a threat, rather than an opportunity. Having your own shop seems threatening only because you don't know how to set it up and run it. Believe me, it can be done and it is far easier to learn than the knowledge you had to absorb during medical school and residency. Having been both a practicing doctor and a practice administrator, I can tell you that administration is a lot easier than rounding in the ICU. However, being a clinician does not teach you how to manage your office. That's why you need to read books such as this one. To learn how to be a shop keeper. Also, knowing how to go into business for yourself is a very important trump card for any doctor. Past experience shows you may very well find yourselves in a salaried job that you don't like. If you rule out private practice, the only way out of this unpleasant situation is to find another salaried job where you may very well run into the same problems again. However, if you know how to open your own office, you have a very important career choice, one you can exercise at any time, a choice that nobody can take away from you.

Is it possible for a resident to enter a career track as a salaried doctor (for example with a group) and finish his career in the same group? Yes, it is possible. Is it likely? No!

Is it possible for a resident to enter a career track working for the Government (VA Hospitals, Indian Hospitals, or armed forces) and finish his career in the same job? Yes, it is possible. Is it likely? No!

Is it possible for a resident to enter an academic career track, become a professor of somethingology and finish his career in academia, without having any contact with private practice? Yes, of course it is. Is it likely? Again the answer is no. **It is much more likely that you will switch jobs more than one time during your career. It is also very likely that you will spend a long portion of your career in your own private office.**

The residency provides you with an excellent opportunity to explore the community in which you did your residency. In my case it was Phoenix. This is a vast and growing city and I think career opportunities for doctors are good. For graduates of a Phoenix residency, it is logical that you should start looking in Phoenix first. If you already know that you would rather work somewhere else, then your search for a job is more complicated. You will have to travel to the new location often to explore. Travel is hard to arrange during residency.

Start looking for jobs during the final year of your residency. Of course, it is never too early to investigate and see what sort of practice appeals to you. However, do not commit yourself until you are a senior resident. In my experience, you need to finish the first half of your residency to get a feel for what you like and don't like.

How to find a salaried position:

The obvious place to start is by asking your residency program director and all attendings you work with for openings they might know about. Word of mouth is the most likely way to your first job. If your prospective employer allows you to moonlight before you start work, try it on for size. It may save you trouble in the future if you discover it is not for you. In addition:

- Discuss possible openings with various community hospitals in the area. You may find a hospital that is willing to assist you in setting up practice near it. You will be expected to admit patients to that particular hospital. In return, it may help you financially and logistically. In fact, if the hospital is owned by a large chain, it may have a dedicated department for helping doctors go into practice. The people working in such departments would assist you with a host of issues, such as contracting with health plans, finding malpractice insurance, cross coverage or personnel.

- Contact known group practices in the area you are considering, even if you don't know any doctors personally. If there is no opening, ask if they know of any other groups that hire.
- Contact large insurance companies that might employ doctors in their own clinics, such as Cigna.
- Contact urgent care centers or emergency medicine groups, if that is a type of job you are considering.
- Contact Government facilities such as VA, Indian Hospital, the military bases, etc.
- Talk to hospitalist groups. You will find that in future medicine will be divided into an outpatient world and an inpatient world. If you enjoy hospital work, consider doing it full time. This has the added advantage of not needing an office of your own.

PEARL OF WISDOM

My prediction is that most doctors will eventually have their own practices. If you take a salaried job in the private sector, for example with a group practice, make sure **the contracts with the insurance plans are in your name, not in the group's name**! Eventually you will want to leave and open your own practice. If you already have contracts in your own name, you can leave the group and take "your" patients with you. Otherwise you have to recredential with all plans from scratch, which takes a long time. More about this issue in future chapters.

Chapter 2:
You are a medical practice, <u>YOU ARE A BUSINESS!</u>

Motto: The cow that's afraid of the butcher becomes a steak neverthe-less.

The motto is meant to illustrate that no matter how afraid you are of private practice, it might happen to you anyway. If you enter private practice you will have to undergo a metamorphosis. You will no longer be "just" a doc. You need to learn to be a businessman. All private practices are businesses. Don't fall pray to the misconception that if you are small you are not a "true" business. It does not matter how small an office you have. Being a small-business man does not mean you can ignore the principles of good business and live in a world of your own. No, sir! **You must complete the metamorphosis from doc to businessman.** I heard doctors say that if you concentrate on practicing good medicine, every-thing else will fall into place. I wish it were so! If it were, you could stop reading now and ask the bookstore for your money back. You need to learn to run your office like a business to succeed.

Consider the following examples. These are real-life questions you will face as a doctor in private practice. You need to acquire the knowl-edge necessary to make rational decisions in cases such as these:

Example 1: You have been in solo private practice for five years. You are busy. You're doing well. One Friday afternoon you decide to take off early. You turn off your beeper and you go The Coffee Plantation. But instead of enjoying a quiet evening of gourmet Java and good music, you run into five other docs you know. They sit down at your table and start to make fun of you because, guess what? **You are the only doc who does not have a satellite office.** Your evening is ruined. You go home and can't sleep all night wondering whether you too, should open a satellite office of your own. After all everybody seems to have one?! Well, what should you do? Follow the crowd, or stay the course?

Example 2: You have been in solo private practice for five years. You are busy. You're doing well. One Friday afternoon you decide to take off early. You turn off your beeper and you go The Coffee Plantation. But instead of enjoying a quiet evening of gourmet Java and good music, you run into five other docs you know! They sit down at your table and start to make fun of you because, guess what? **You are the only doc who does not have a PA working for him.** Your evening is ruined. You go home and can't sleep all night wondering whether you too, should hire a PA right quick. After all everybody seems to have one?! Well, what should you do? Follow the crowd, or keep things as they are?

Example 3: You have been in solo private practice for five years. You are busy. You're doing well. One day, when you are busy seeing patients, a hardware rep comes to your office to show you a new, portable, user-friendly ultrasound machine. It is cool, small and looks like a good gadget to impress patients with (you are a modern doc after all). It can ultrasound any part of the body you can think of: thyroid, vessels, gall bladder, you name it. The rep points out that if you buy it, the **purchase price will lower your taxable income** (business expense!) and he will give you a good deal at $20,000. Should you buy it?

Things to know before you can make a rational decision: THE BUSINESS PRINCIPLES UPON WHICH YOUR PRACTICE IS FOUNDED

When you are in private practice, you are <u>in business</u>. I know I repeat myself, but I sense you don't believe me (yet!). Many doctors think of their practices as a means to serve humanity rather than a way to make money. Words like "profit", "bottom line", "writing black numbers", "watching expenses", are often considered dirty talk by doctors. The prevailing attitude is that the lofty medical profession does not lower itself to such matters as counting dough! This attitude is wrong. You must think like a businessman and follow good business principles. If you do, you will make more money and work fewer hours than the doctor next door who does not.

Characteristics of businesses (all of them!):

- **They must be profitable.** If there is no profit, they are forced to close. A business that cannot pay its rent will be evicted whether it is a doctor or an airline.
- **All businesses are hierarchical structures with one single boss.** Obviously, large companies have complicated administrative structures, but ultimately there is only one person in charge on whose desk the buck stops. The most important reasons why most large group practices have failed is that there was nobody in charge. They tried to rule themselves by consensus. All doctors were equal partners; there were many chiefs, but no Indians.
- **You are the boss only if you have the power to fire everyone in the business.** Being a "partner", such as in a group practice, does not make you a boss. In fact it is essential that a group practice appoints a boss rather than be ruled by consensus. More about this

very important issue in future chapters.

- **All businesses are subject to market forces.** It is very important to understand what they are and how they affect you. Roughly speaking, the thing that is rare (such as Gold) is dear and the thing that is plentiful is cheap (such as sand). However, this applies to far more complex matters. Think about family practice. In the past, a family doc worked in the office, admitted his own patients to the hospital and also delivered babies. However, in spite of this relentless schedule, the pay of a general practitioner was nothing to e-mail home about. Specialists made much more money and worked less hours. Given the difficult work and low pay, fewer students chose family practice as a career. Eventually, there were not enough family docs to fill all the positions, i.e., FPs became rare. Next, their income started to go up and the workload decreased. Admissions are now often handled by hospitalists. Babies are delivered by OB-GYN doctors. As a consequence, more students chose family practice as a career, thereby increasing the number of FPs in practice. This is the direct result of market forces. Needless to say, the process could be reversed too. If more medical students go into family practice, eventually FPs will become plentiful again. Their incomes will likely decrease and the cycle will repeat itself.
- **All businesses are subject to economic cycles.** These are completely beyond your control. However, since you know they occur, you can prepare for bad years during good years; for example by stashing money away for "rainy days". Because of economic cycles, your income will not be stagnant, nor will it increase every year. You will have good years and bad years, even if you are a perfect businessman.
- Roughly speaking, businesses are divided into 2 broad categories: **manufacturers** (think of them as businesses that make something you can hold in your hand, such as a computer) and **service providers** (think of them as businesses that do something that cannot be held in your hand, such as airlines, which provide transportation). A doctor is a service provider.
- **All businesses have products** (in your case the advice you give your patients), **customers** (not only your patients, but also other doctors who refer to you), and **vendors** (such as your landlord). It is important to recognize this because throughout your lifetime in business, you will need to work on refining your product, on satisfying your customers and on lowering your vendor expenses.

As far as the characteristics noted above, doctors' offices are exactly like any other business. They differ, however, in other ways.

Characteristics of doctor's offices (which do not necessarily apply to other businesses):

- **The owner is the worker <u>and</u> the manager**. Picture a large corporation, for example Ford Motor Co. It is owned by the stock holders. It is run by managers, who are not the same people as the stock holders (Of course, nobody can stop a manager from buying stock, but that is not the point). The workers, i.e. the guys who actually make the cars, are a third group of people distinct from the other two. If the boss (CEO) is on the factory floor or not, cars continue to be manufactured and sold. That means the company makes money whether the boss is on the premises or not. In contrast, a medical doctor is not only owner, but also worker. If he does not see patients, there is no money coming in at all.
- **Often you hear that a corporation must "grow" to be viable**. Medical offices are not sentenced to the "grow or perish" requirement. You hear all the time how a business is doomed if it does not grow. I am happy to report as a doctor you are not subject to this pressure. Once you have a full practice, see that you keep it full and leave it at that.
- **You don't need to convince your clients that they need your services**. They are already convinced. This is an advantage many other businesses do not have. Most businesses need to convince the public to come in and buy. Vineyards, airlines, pet stores, all depend on the public's willingness to use their products and services. Do you really need to drink wine? Or travel to Timbuktu? Or have a dog? You can live your life without wine, travel and dogs. But you cannot live your life without medical care. If you break a leg, you cannot ignore it and hope it will mend itself. You need to see a doctor. Consequently, doctors don't need to advertise very much. They don't need to convince the public of the need to see a doctor. When the client (patient) walks into your practice, he has already convinced himself that he needs your services. People go to stores, just to see what's for sale. Many times they leave without buying anything. Nobody comes to the doctor's office just to see what's going on. A person entering a medical practice will buy the doctor's service. Nobody leaves without a charge.

Answers to examples: based on the principles discussed above, let's answer the examples discussed at the beginning.

Example 1: opening a satellite office.

Since you cannot see patients in two places at the same time, i.e., make money in two locations at the same time, what is the point of a satellite office? A second location is going to increase your expenses, but will it also increase you income? Very likely not.

If you have a full practice at your regular location pat yourself on the back: you are a success. You cannot have two full practices in two places. Moreover, you do not get paid for traveling between the two offices. It is perfectly reasonable to strive for a full practice in one single location and not pursue further growth. You can make a living from one practice indefinitely.

If you don't have as many patients as you would like at your regular location, you should examine the causes very carefully before you jump to the wrong conclusion. The knee jerk reaction is "I need to open an additional office to tap into another market". Don't! Instead, analyze with your feet in cold water why the patients don't come to you.

Possibilities include:

- **Make sure there are enough patients** in the geographic area where you practice. If there are too many doctors, you are not going to have a full practice. For example, don't start a new practice in Beverly Hills. I guarantee there are more than enough doctors there. If there are not enough patients to feed all the doctors in your area, move to a new location; but move the whole office, don't open a second one.
- **Make sure you are contracted with all relevant insurance plans.** If 40% of people in the area are insured with BlueCross/BlueShield, hurry up and sign a contract with them! Provided, of course, BC/BS offers a good contract. Contracting with health plans is a complex subject that will be addressed separately.
- **You may need to work on your people skills.** Perhaps the patients do not like you. Patients have no way to gauge your medical skills. Instead, they judge your personality. You may have won the Nobel Prize, but if the patients do not like your bed-side manner, your waiting room will be empty.
- **Advertise.** This too, will be addressed separately.
- Consider **offering a service that no other doctor offers** in the area, such as house calls, late hours or cosmetic procedures.

If you truly have too many patients, your options include:

- **Closing the practice to new patients.** This is done all the time, and for good reason, because the alternatives are in my judgment less appealing (see below).
- **Hire a PA.** But be CAREFUL! A PA or a nurse practitioner will be very expensive. Make sure you have added your numbers correctly. See discussion of example 2 below.
- **Hire another doctor,** or take a "partner". After all "growing" group practices do this all the time. However, don't deceive yourself; this is an <u>extremely</u> difficult undertaking. Of course, it is possible to find a good fit, a doctor with whom you can work and who does not mind being your subordinate. But the chance is small and the potential headaches are numerous. Conflicts typically arise when the new doc comes in as partner. Who is in charge now? Remember, businesses are hierarchical structures and there needs to be one single boss. Having two bosses in one practice doesn't work. Typically, when there are several "equal" partners, nobody is in charge any more and the office is left in the hands of an office manager. This manager becomes essentially unsupervised; a situation that should be avoided at all costs. More about this in later chapters.

Example 2: hiring a PA.

This first thing to keep in mind is that a PA (or nurse practitioner, RN, etc.) is going to be a <u>very big expense</u>, in the order of tens of thousands of dollars per year. That is a truck load of money for a small business like your practice! Remember, the salary will not be the only expense. You may need to modify the office to give the PA space to practice; you'll have higher premiums for malpractice insurance, worker's comp insurance, office liability insurance and health insurance. Your supervisory duties will be more complex.

The argument heard most frequently regarding PAs is this: "I hired a PA to see my low paying capitated patients, so I can concentrate on the higher paying fee-for-service ones". The answer to this argument is as follows:

- **You should <u>never</u> sign a capitated contract**. All your contracts should be fee-for-service. If an insurance only offers you a capitated contract, my advice would be to walk away. Capitation is an exceptionally complex contract that requires a lot of knowledge and experience to be profitable. However, the most important reason why such a contract should be avoided is because it generates a misalignment of financial interests between doctor and patient. By signing a flat fee agreement, the patient has an incentive to come to you as often as possible. All he pays is the copay. Your incentive however, is to see the patient as rarely as possible to make money from the flat fee. More about this in the future, but having capitated contracts is not a reason to hire a PA but it is a reason to turn them into fee-for-service contracts.

- **Make sure you truly have enough patients** to keep you <u>and</u> the PA busy. A lot of doctors deceive themselves into thinking their practices have become too big. In fact they "feel" too busy because they are disorganized. Adding the PA expense will only make them poorer.
- **Review your contracts with the health plans** if you truly have too many patients. Please note I said if you "truly" have too many patients, not if you just think you do! Renegotiate the low paying contracts first and cancel those that do not want to improve reimbursement to reduce your workload. If you are a well established, profitable practice, getting rid of the low payers is a very reasonable step.
- **The PA will inevitably "dilute" the name brand**. After all when a patient comes to you, he will want to actually see you. Some patients do not mind seeing a PA, but are your patients like that? Remember, nobody goes to the Mercedes dealer to buy a Ford.

Hiring a PA can be a very reasonable thing to do. But you must do your homework first. Financially, this is a very big decision. There is no such thing as "let's hire a PA" emergency.

Example 3: buying the ultrasound machine, or indeed anything for the practice.

PEARL OF WISDOM

I want to establish emphatically a cardinal principle of good business: **NEVER BUY ANYTHING SIMPLY BECAUE IT IS TAX DEDUCTIBLE.** Most doctors don't realize that "tax deductible" means Uncle Sam will reimburse you for only a fraction of your expense, i.e., by an amount equal to your tax bracket. For example, if your mortgage is $10,000 a year and you are in the 30% bracket, you will get back about $3,000. Uncle Sam will <u>never</u> reimburse you for the entire expense. Buying a tax deductible thing is still an expense.

Everything you buy for your practice must help raise your bottom line!

There are no exceptions to this. This applies to a cheap item such as a pencil and to expensive items such as the ultrasound machine. It is folly to drop money right and left without calculating the expected profit from your investment. Don't simply buy expensive things to show others how well you are doing. It is not good business to rent a palatial office just to show what a big shot you are. Also, never buy anything under pressure from a salesman. There is no such thing as a "buy this US now" emergency!

If you believe that you could make money from the US machine, do the following:

- Over the next 6 months **count the number of patients who would have required an US.** However, keep in mind that the act of observation changes the object under observation. You will likely find more patients in need of an US than there really are because you will be "looking" for them. Remember that to be reimbursed for the US, it will have to be "medically necessary", otherwise the insurance will deny payment. You can bet their idea of "medically necessary" is far more stringent than yours!
- **Calculate the reimbursement from your biggest contracted insurance plans.**
- **Multiply the two numbers above.** Make sure the US will "pay for itself" within twelve to eighteen months, otherwise don't buy it.
- **Don't forget to include the cost of learning** how to use the US. Most likely the manufacturer will send you to a course at their expense, if you insist. However, even if you don't pay for the course, while you are away from the practice, you are not generating income. This is the same as incurring an expense.
- **Consider leasing it,** but make sure you can return it to the manufacturer at the end of the leasing contract without incurring additional costs. Leasing contracts are notoriously cavernous. You may find yourself separated from a lot more dollars than you thought initially.
- If you buy it, definitely look for a **used** one.
- Consider **sharing the cost** with other doctors.

Chapter 3: COUNTDOWN TO OPENING DAY

Motto: Caution is the mother of your career.

If you are a resident at the time you read this, picture yourself in the future, say two - three years after the end of your residency. You decide to open your own practice, now what? Before answering this question, let's establish first what is likely to happen to you after residency. Remember, my prediction is that most of you will work as salaried doctors first before opening your own practices. There are good reasons why you should not rush into opening your practice immediately after residency.

Don't open a practice immediately after residency

The most important reasons are:

- **You are too busy** during residency to go through the 1001 steps necessary for opening a practice. It can be done, but I would steer you away from such a course of action.
- **You are too green.** Life experience is very important in business. Medical school and residency do not teach you to be "street wise". You need a dose of street wisdom to succeed in business.
- **You are too poor.** Ideally, you should have time to stabilize your financial situation, i.e., pay off all your school loans and save money in anticipation of having your own practice. Very likely, you will need to borrow some money to open your shop. If you already have debt, banks may not be so eager to extend more credit.

What should you do after residency?

Rest!

After residency you'll be exhausted. In fact you'll be so tired, you won't realize how tired you are until you have rested and you begin to feel like a "normal" human being again. If you want my advice, **take six months off!** For two reasons:

- You need time to study for the boards and you can't work <u>and</u> study effectively. It is important to pass your boards on the first try since you don't want to go through this examination again a year later.

- You should rest and start your new career rested, not tired. If somebody wants to hire you to start work within two-three weeks of finishing residency, just say no! There will be other opportunities. Fortunately this is not a job market where you must jump at the first offer.

No, your eyes are not playing tricks on you, I really wrote **sixs months**! It is the last time in your entire life when you can goof-off at your leisure. Later you'll have a career, children, etc., and they do not give time off, even if you had the money to do so. Finance your vacation by working prn in an ER or urgent care center if you need extra money. Alternatively, borrow the money. Incidentally, this is the <u>only</u> time I would advocate borrowing money for vacations in the course of your entire life. My personal conviction is that you truly need that much time off to recover from the residency and medical school. I strongly advocate that you do it.

Take a salaried job

Often your first salaried job will be with a group practice. Typically, a "growing" group of three or four doctors feels it needs the extra body to handle the hoards of patients knocking on their door. After working there for about two years, you realize that it is time to put what you learned in this book to use and open your own shop. Things may not be going as promised in the group.

Typical reasons why salaried jobs go wrong

Let's use the example with the five man group practice again to examine some typical occurrences:

- **The group has 5 doctors, but no boss**. This is a scenario encountered all too frequently. The "group" consists of five separate practices that share an office, the equipment and the personnel. They all share the costs equally, i.e., each is expected to pay one fifth of the expenses. A five man group may not sound like a very big business, given that the mega-groups of yesteryear had two hundred and more doctors. But remember, the size of the business has nothing to do with the need to adhere to good business principles. Since all five practices are "equal", in reality nobody is in charge. There may be one doc who likes to dabble in administrative duties, but in reality the group is in the hands of a hired office manager. In a larger business, that guy would be called a CEO. The problem with this arrangement is that the manager is essentially unsupervised. Not only that, but the manager cannot overrule the doctors. They are the owners. They sign his paycheck. If a doctor wants to do something boneheaded, the manager cannot stop him. For example, let's say one of the five docs thinks his patients are sicker than the other four doctors' patients. He may say something like, "I need an additional nurse to help me deal with these very sick patients", and he asks the group to share the costs of this new hire used by him alone. Or another doctor doesn't want to work as hard as everybody else so he balks at paying his fifth of the costs. His argument would be, "I'm free to work as hard as I please. If I am happy with less money, that's my prerogative. But since I earn less then you four, I should pay a lesser share of the costs. After all, one who is in the office fewer hours generates fewer expenses". And so on! You get the picture.

As you will see later, the person who runs the practice makes or breaks it. In our example, since the manager is just another hired employee (albeit an important one), he will work only as hard as necessary to keep his job. His job is to be the watchdog for the owners and to make sure the shop is run well. But the key question is "**WHO WATCHES THE WATCHDOG?**" Normally, in a regular business, the CEO is watched by the owners. But our five docs are busy seeing patients and don't understand they need to take time for administrative work.

The problem outlined above reveals that the manager is boss over the little folk (receptionist, RN), but not over the doctors. That is a problem that may spell disaster for the group. In my judgment, a group practice of any size, be it five docs or five hundred, needs to appoint a true boss. Call him a CEO, managing partner, or whatever title you want. This person needs to have knowledge of business administration and should have the power to lead the entire operation. Remember, my definition of a boss is a person who can fire everybody under him, including the doctors. Especially the doctors! The big question then becomes who will supervise this boss? This is a question that does not have an ideal answer, in my judgment. This is the reason why I advise you to open a solo practice, rather than join group. In a solo practice, the question of who the boss is solves itself: it is you! If you have four other friends (other four solo practitioners) with whom you would like to practice, there is nothing to stop four solo practices from sharing call and helping each other in any conceivable fashion. But beware! Once these four "friends" join together to form a group practice, hallelujah! Disaster is near.

PEARL OF WISDOM

When in doubt, always go for a solo practice! It is far easier to find other docs with whom to share call than to find other docs with whom you can form a functioning business.

- **Your contracts with health plans are in the group's name.** After two years or so with the group, you have had enough and want to go out on your own. But you forgot a very important point I made in chapter one: your contracts with the insurance plans are in the group's name rather than in your name! Ooooops! Big ooooops! You can only hang up your shingle if you have contracts with insurances. Otherwise, you'll have no patients. Once you separate from the group, from the point of view of the plans, you stop existing. Very likely they will require you to go through the credentialing process again as a solo practitioner. You will argue, "I was seeing your patients when I was part of the group, why can't you give me an individual contract right quick, after all you already know me". The insurance plans will counter, "That's your point of view. For us, once you have separated from the group, you are no longer credentialed and you need to start from scratch". The contracting process is very long, laborious and requires some experience. During this time you're going to need to make money to pay the rent. How are you going to make money if you have no patients? More about contracting later.

PEARL OF WISDOM

When you sign up with a group, insist that the **contracts with the health plans be in your own name,** under your own tax ID number, rather than in the group's name and the group's tax ID number. That way when you separate from the group, you'll have patients from day one. In fact, you'll continue seeing "your" patients from the group. I would go one step further; I would say that it is acceptable to have signed lousy contracts (for example, low reimbursement), as long as they are in your name. Lousy contracts can be renegotiated. During this time you can still see patients. But if the contracts are in the group's name, well...

- **The group does not let you see your EOBs or, worse, it does not let you see how their expenses are calculated.** You must see your EOBs. Do so even if you are a salaried doc, who has a salary guarantee. Looking at the EOBs will tell you some important things:

-**Does the group actually send out the bills on time?** If not, they are behind in collecting and you should bail out today, rather than tomorrow. Remember, if bills are not sent out to insurances you will never get paid. You would have worked for free.

-**How much do you actually get paid?** Compare your reimbursement with what it says in the contract with the health plan. If the payment is wrong dispute it.

If the group refuses to let you see their expenses, don't work for them. There is something very fishy! There is no reason in the world why a group should not let a prospective partner see the expense accounts. After all, they want you to pay your share. A share of what? You simply have to know. "Trust us, we do it right" is not an acceptable answer.

PEARL OF WISDOM

There is no "trust us" in business. This is not to say you must be paranoid and suspect fraud behind every tree. However, you should take the attitude "trust, but verify". If somebody faults you for that, do not do business with him.

- **The group insists you sign a non-compete clause.** Non-compete clauses state that, if you leave the group, you will not open a practice of your own nearby. Usually there is a time limit, for example two years. This means that after two years you can open your own shop, even across the street from your previous group. The purpose of these clauses is to ensure that a doctor who separates from the group does not siphon-off patients who were cared for by the group. Remember, my theory is that you will not last long with the group. **Consequently, you must prepare your exit at the time you are hired.** What you want is precisely what the non-compete clause tries to prevent. You want time to gather patients of your own, patients who will then follow you to your solo practice once you separate from the group. The patients will not follow you if your solo shop is far from the group location. That means, you must open your practice near the group. I would counsel you to make every effort to avoid non-compete clauses.

- **Your employment contract is vague and poorly written.** If you take a job with a group, you must **review your employment contract very, very carefully.** You will need the help of a good lawyer for this. Remember, the contract needs to cover not only the conditions of your employment, but also the manner in which you can separate from your employer. **It must allow you to take your patients with you when you leave.** If you open your own practice and have no patients, you're in trouble. It takes years to build a practice from scratch.

Your employment contract will have to be reviewed by a lawyer, as mentioned. However, dealing with lawyers is a learned art.

Working with lawyers (takes experience)

Conventional wisdom has it that the legal profession harbors a high percentage of crooks and liars. This makes good bar-room conversation, nothing else. The difficulty you will encounter with lawyers is this: the lawyer **may solve the problem brought to his attention, but will often create a new one in the process.** After all, lawyers are in business too and want to generate more of it. Since you are green, you won't know if the new, "lawyer generated" matter is relevant or just a way to ensure billable hours. My advice is this:

- **Limit the scope of the lawyer's job.** Say, "I am here for you to review this contract. I want you to pay particular attention to contracts with health plans, non-compete clause, etc." Don't say, "I want you to teach me how to tell a good contract from a bad one". The latter is an invitation to open ended billings.

- **Limit the time you allow the lawyer to work on your problem.** Say, "your budget for this job is X billable hours" and then insist the work is done within budget. As a guideline, if it takes you an hour to read a contract, allow your lawyer 30 minutes to review it. After all, he does this sort of thing for a living and can be expected to finish faster than you.

- **Always communicate with your lawyer in writing**. My favorite way is through e-mail. I found that lawyers are very slow to return phone calls. "Hi Chris, I'm returning your call from last year". I found e-mails are answered quickly. Keep all e-mail communication with lawyers for eternity, never discard it. Also, keep your e-mails short because lawyers charge you for reading your e-mail!

My usual approach is to write a letter like this:

"Dear legal eagle:

Attached to this e-mail you will find the contract offered to me by "Germs-R-Us Medical Group". I would like you to review it and address the following issues:

- a. will I be expected to bring my own germs to work, or will the group provide them
- b. do I get to build up my practice and then leave, taking my patients with me
- c. etc., etc.

Please let me know in advance if you think this job will take more than half an hour of your time."

Typically, I get the answer I'm looking for, but also I get baited with other stuff. For example, the lawyer says the contract needs to be amended and makes some suggestions. He then bills me for the half an hour allowed. After which comes the second act. This is the "let's-drum-up-more-business" part of the encounter. He'll say something like, "Chris, did you ever think about asset protection? You know doctors are rich people and you need to protect your assets in case of a lawsuit. As it happens, I am an expert on the subject. For only $10,000 in initial fees and $300 a month for eternity, I'll protect your assets better than a rabid pit-bull". The advisable answer to this bait should be, "Thank you so much for your farsighted wisdom. I'll get back to you".

This tactic is only natural. Don't be upset at the lawyers for doing it. Every shop owner wants to generate more business. Instead of complaining, you should take it to heart. When you see a patient, ask him: "Mr. Smith, I have been your doctor for two years, but I have never met your wife. Did you know I do pap smears, too? Maybe you will allow me the privilege of caring for your entire family. I would be delighted".

Incidentally, never ask your lawyer to write your employment contract from scratch. That guarantees endless billings. The guy will smell boat payments. Always ask your potential employer to present you with their standard contract and only ask your lawyer to review it.

Preparing your exit: practical pointers

Let's go back to my original prediction. After residency, your first job is going to be a salaried position, most likely with a group. Let's also restate the second part of my theory: your first job will not be your last. You will not stay in your first job until retirement. Very likely you will change jobs more than once. Since I believe job changes are inevitable, **when you get hired, you must prepare your exit!** Here is a summary of the most important points:

- **Form your own business entity and get the employer to "hire" the business, rather than you as an individual.** This allows a smoother departure, should you want to open a practice of your own later. It also allows you a high degree of operating independence, even while you are technically on salary. For example, you can buy equipment and hire personnel without asking for permission from the employer. This, of course, assumes you will pay for said equipment and personnel out of your own pocket.

- **Get insurance contracts in <u>your</u> name.** Not in your employer's name, not in your business's name, but in your own name. That way, you can start a practice of your own and have access to patients from day one. This is essential. It does no good to open your own shop first and then chase after insurance contracts. That takes too long. Meanwhile, you have to pay your bills.
- **Avoid non-compete clauses.** When you open your shop, you want it to be near the old one, so your patients will continue with you. Consequently, avoid clauses which dictate when and where you can open your office.
- **Get your employer to pay for your malpractice "tail".** More about this very important issue in future chapters. For now, remember that tails are expensive. Best to sock this to your employer.
- **While you work on salary, build a practice!** You must have patients of your own, patients who come to you because they want to see you, not because you happen to be part of a group. This should be as large a number of patients as you can possibly handle. For example, a family doc should have about 2000 – 2500 patients of his own. These patients will later form the foundation of your own practice. Obviously, if you work at a VA hospital, you cannot expect those patients to follow you to your own shop, because they are tied to the VA system. But if you work for a private group, "your" patients will very likely follow you to your new location, if it is not too far.

PEARL OF WISDOM

If you have bad luck and you find yourself working for the worst possible group practice, don't despair. **At the very least you will learn how not to run your office,** which is very useful knowledge indeed! In fact, if you are going to see bad management in action, it might as well be in somebody else's business, rather than your own.

Chapter 4:
GETTING SERIOUS ABOUT HANGING UP YOUR SHINGLE

Motto: Even sky scrapers started out as basements.

First things first: FINANCING, COMPANIES, CODING, COMPUTERS, CONTRACTS!

We live in a capitalist economy (fortunately!), so the first step for any new business is to obtain capital. You will need enough money to cover your expenses until you become profitable. I expect you will have contracts with insurance plans in place at the time you open the office. If you do, you will have patients from day one. Still, you will need to finance the practice for about six months. You will need enough money to:

- **Pay for your own life**, which will not be put on hold, just because you are now opening a practice. Add up all your normal expenses and don't forget the less obvious ones, like vacations. After six months you'll be ready for a couple of weeks in Hawaii, I guarantee it. Include a strategic reserve, for unexpected occurrences. I would recommend 15% of your regular expenses.
- **Pay for all start-up costs**, i.e., one-time expenditures that will not recur, such as buying equipment and having it installed.
- **Pay the day-to-day costs** of the business until you start to get paid by insurances. Such costs include rent, payroll and insurance. Typically, it takes three-four months before you will make enough money to become less dependent on loans.

In my view, by the end of the sixth month you should no longer need to dip into your line of credit to pay for the day-to-day costs. By the ninth month you should have paid back your loans and be up and running. You should make a living from your practice. If by the end of the ninth month you are still living on borrowed money, things have gone very wrong! I cannot say it often enough: **THIS ASSUMES YOU WILL HAVE PATIENTS FROM DAY ONE, THAT IS, YOU HAVE ALL YOUR INSURANCE CONTRACTS IN PLACE BEFORE YOU OPEN FOR BUSINESS.** If you open and don't have contacts, you opened too soon! This is why it is so important to have contracts in your name early in your career. In fact, the banks will look far more favorably on your request for financing, if you have contracts. The banks will certainly ask you how you will get customers.

If you open a practice with zero patients, be prepared to live on borrowed money for a long time. It is impossible to predict how long it will take to fill a practice with patients. It depends on many factors, such as your specialty, location, business skills, and ability to attract and keep customers. The short answer is, don't do it. Find the patients first and then open an office.

Finding the patients before opening the office may sound counterintuitive. Don't shops have to be open for customers to walk in? Not necessarily. When Wal-Mart opens a new store you can be certain the management asked themselves "Do we have enough potential buyers at the planned location?". If the answer is negative, there will be no new store. For a doctor, the best way to find the patients before opening his own practice is by working for a group first. The patients cared for while employed by the group will probably follow the doctor to his new office.

Financing

The most obvious place to look for money is your regular bank. You should look for the lowest interest, of course, but there are other things to consider as well.

What sort of loan should you get?

In my experience, a "**revolving line of credit**" is the most practical type of loan. This works very much like a credit card. Let's say the bank agrees to give you $100,000. From that point on, you have access to $100,000. But you only pay interest if you use the money and only on the amount actually used. There is no obligation to use all 100,000 at one time. Let's say in the fist month you use $30,000. You only pay interest on $30,000 and not on the remaining $70,000. You can pay it off any time without penalty. In fact you should do just that, pay it off as fast as possible. After that, keep the line of credit alive for as long as the bank will let you. That way you have access to capital whenever needed, but you don't pay interest until you actually use it. The interest for this line of credit is higher than a mortgage, but it is easier to use and the maintenance fees are small. Ask your bank for advice regarding the best type of loan. Talk to an experienced credit person at the bank, not the teller. They may steer you to an even better product. Remember, just like anything else, credit products change from time to time.

How much should you borrow?

In 2004, you should obtain $100,000 – 150,000. If the bank is willing to give you more, take it. Get a loan that only requires you to pay interest on the amount actually used, not on the total amount at your disposal. That is why the revolving line of credit is such a good example.

How is this sum calculated? A good rule of thumb is that your practice is going to cost you $10,000 a month. Add $5,000 a month for your personal expenses and you get $60,000 for your practice and $30,000 for you for the first six months. Add start up costs and financial emergencies and you can't go wrong if you have $150,000 available.

Coding

Repeat after me: **CODING IS MONEY, CODING IS MONEY**. Coding is an important subject, which you should take very seriously. **It cannot be learned "on the fly"** because it is too complex. Remember, the codes are information insurances use to pay you. If you undercode, miss modifiers, or bundle, you cheat yourself out of money that is rightfully yours. If you overcode, you are stealing. Coding must be done exactly right to ensure maximum payment for your efforts. Moreover, knowledge of coding allows you to tailor each patient encounter to maximize reimbursement. For example, some insurance plans don't pay for a history and physical done on the day you removed a mole. They only pay for the mole removal, saying that the H&P is a natural part of the procedure. Even if you apply the correct modifiers, payment is nevertheless denied. This is one of the 1001 games insurances play to lower reimbursement. To get around this, do the H&P first and bring the patient back for the mole removal on another day. That way you get paid for both.

Coding must be learned from expert coders, who do it for a living. Many community colleges offer evening classes. You can enroll while you work on salary in preparation of opening your own office. The complete coding curriculum requires courses in other subjects, such as anatomy and medical terminology. You can ask the college to waive those requirements, since you had enough anatomy already.

After you learn to code, please do not forget about it. **Go to coding CME every year** to stay current. Ask your state medical association if they provide coding CME.

PEARL OF WISDOM

Learn how to code and you will have money. Ignore it and I've wasted my efforts on you! Also, do not ever leave the coding to your staff. That is a very big mistake. **You must do your own coding!** Typically, doctors dictate their notes and when the dictation comes back, the biller codes the encounter and sends out the bill. Do not do that. Billers are notorious undercoders. Undercoding will cost you tens of thousands in dollars every year, money that is rightfully yours. **Coding is the doctor's responsibility**. If an insurance or Government agency ever investigates your coding methods, you cannot hide behind your biller. Asking your staff to code your encounters is an unreasonable burden for them. Remember, you were in the room with the patient, not your biller. You know what code applies best!

Computers

If at this stage in your life you don't have working knowledge of computers, you have a very serious handicap. Don't treat them like lepers! You must know how to use computers very well to succeed in business. They are the cheapest and most reliable workers you will ever have. In modern offices there are many transactions which simply cannot be done by hand, for example billings. You must:

- **Have working knowledge of Windows (or Mac) and word processing**. You must know your way around well enough to troubleshoot minor errors, such as why a read/write CD no longer lets you read and write to it.
- **Know how to hook-up external gizmos**, such as hard drives or scanners.
- **Know how to use the Internet** in your sleep. Nowadays, not knowing to navigate the Internet is like not knowing how to drive a car. It is unthinkable for the modern businessman.
- **Have a good grasp of computer security**, especially how it pertains to the Internet.

If at the time you read this you are computer illiterate, you are in trouble. No matter what job you have later, it will be a very serious handicap. Take a beginner's class at a community college, buy yourself a computer and get to work! Incidentally, you must know how to type using ten fingers blindly (without looking at the keyboard). This can be learned in two weeks, using your computer, taking a one hour lesson a day. Of course you cannot do this during residency, but you can do it during your six month vacation afterwards.

Your business entity

In my view, the only entity you should consider is a **Professional Limited Liability Company**. This entity is very easy and cheap to set up, and requires no maintenance. It is "ignored" for tax purposes. You still fill out your 1040 and attach Schedule C, where the financials of your PLLC are dealt with. The LLCs are very well described in

Form your own limited liability company by Anthony Mancuso. Publisher: Nolo (this is a publisher of many business related and legal advice books) ISBN: 0-87337-797-4

Alternatively you could form a C-corporation, or S-corporation and who knows what else. But why would you? Especially for the beginner, the LLC is ideal.

PEARL OF WISDOM

Lest you think that all is milk any honey in the land of business entities: **the words "limited liability" don't mean you can escape professional liability (read: malpractice lawsuits)** by hiding behind a business entity. No matter what entity you form, your risk of being sued for malpractice is the same. The limitation in liability applies only to your creditors, but not your patients!

Contracts

Patients rarely come to the doctor with the express intention of paying cash for your services. The vast majority will want you to bill their insurance. Therefore, before potential customers can become real customers, you need to jump through some hoops.

Contracts with whom?

You need to contract with all the **relevant insurance plans**, i.e., those with large patient populations in your area. Some examples of large insurers include Blue Cross Blue Shield, Aetna, Cigna, Humana, United HealthCare, PacifiCare, Medicare, Medicaid and Workers' Comp. In addition, **strongly consider joining IPAs,** because they allow you access to a multitude of small plans, plans that are too small to contract with individually. Some insurers offer indemnity plans, which allow their patients to go to any doctor. These are great to contract with because either they don't require a contract at all, or have very straightforward contracts. Medicare is the biggest indemnity plan of them all, however, it is not the best paying one.

If you want a complete list of the plans you should have contracts with, **ask doctors who already practice in your area for their lists.** I cannot possibly give you a complete list here. Also, **discuss with those doctors the pros and contras of contracting with each plan and IPA. More importantly, ask them why they do not contract with certain plans.** For example, surgeons practicing in Phoenix like Blue Cross, but would rather not deal with Medicaid plans (known as AHCCCS in Arizona). Medicaid pay for surgeons is low and delays are common. However, the answer may very well be different for an OB doctor. I hear many OB docs say they love the AHCCCS plans. What plans you sign up with as a beginner, is a judgment call. Later on, after a few years in practice, you can reassess your contracts and drop those that did not live up to your expectations.

Health Insurance Plans

What is a health plan anyway? The principle upon which all insurances are based is the following: a large population takes prophylactic measures against a calamity. Let's say the calamity is a house fire. The insurance company calculates the odds of a house fire in a particular community and then offers to rebuild the houses that burn down. How are such policies priced? Let's say there are 100 houses in town. Let's say past experience show that one house burns down every year. Let's further assume that each house costs $ 100,000 to rebuild. The insurance knows it will incur costs of $100,000 per year. Therefore, it must charge its customers $100,000/year plus administrative costs. If it only has one customer, that person pays all of the $100 grand. If it has 100 customers, then each one pays $1,000 per year for his house fire insurance. Problems arise when there are more losses than anticipated. If two houses burn down in one year, the insurance will have to double its premium. In years when there are fewer losses, the price goes down. This is, of course, an oversimplification. In reality the calculations are very complicated and require large data bases. In summary, **those not affected by the calamity, pay the repair costs of those whom lighting struck.** In case of health insurance, **people currently healthy pay the treatment costs of those currently sick.**

Contracts about what?

All contracts with health insurances have the following in common:

- **They define who enters into contract with whom**. For example, Aetna as an insurer enters into contract with your practice, "Germs-R-US, PLLC".
- **They define each other's duties:** you are going to treat the patients and Aetna is going to pay you for your service.
- **They define how much you are going to be paid,** how quickly you need to submit your bills and how to resolve disputes.
- They establish a series of **requirements for the contractual relationship to be valid:** Aetna needs to be a licensed insurance in good standing, abiding by all relevant laws. You, the doctor, need to be a graduate of a recognized specialty training program (such as family practice), have an unrestricted license to practice medicine, a DEA number, an office, equipment and staff needed to

see patients, hold malpractice insurance, have arranged for cross coverage, etc.

- They go on and on like a bad dream about all sorts **of legalese stuff** that needs to be included, such as the need to conform with laws against discrimination, Medicare guidelines, etc., etc.

The important stuff: your reimbursement

Most contracts are many pages long. However, in my experience, the only important stuff is **the pay**. Usually, it is just a paragraph, or an attachment. All the other stuff included in a contract is less important to the solo practitioner, in my judgment.

The other stuff

Contracts outline the rules by which two entities agree to do business together. The contracts gather dust on a shelf as long as the business relationship is good. They are dusted off when there is a conflict. The parties then refer to the contract to resolve their dispute. For you, as a solo practitioner, the only disputes you are likely to have with health insurances are about pay. This is why I would counsel you to **watch carefully all the contractual provisions pertaining to pay** and not waste energy on things that are not likely to become contentious. Of course, theoretically, everything in a contract is important, in case of conflict. Some experts would counsel you to avoid anything that puts you at a disadvantage. My answer is that you are very unlikely to have any dispute with a health insurance other than about pay. In my judgment, it is better to concentrate on getting a good deal where it matters and leave the other things alone. I don't think you'll have time to negotiate away all murky things in all contracts with all insurances. You need to prioritize!

Stuff that can be negotiated, stuff that cannot

This differs from insurance to insurance. I have dealt with plans that say "our entire contract is a take-it-or-leave-it proposition". This is rare, but it makes your job easy: either you sign, or you don't. Again, in my judgment, the pay is the only part of the contract that's worth the sweat. When the contract is negotiable, concentrate on the pay and leave the other issues alone.

Every contract has provisions in it that are not negotiable. For example, inclusions required by law which you cannot change. Others may not be required by law, but are so ingrained, that you cannot change them either, for example the need to carry malpractice insurance.

Types of contracts

The only contract you should ever sign is a **fee-for-service contract**. This means you only submit a bill when you saw a patient and only for the things you actually did to (or for!) that patient. There are other types of contracts, such as flat fee agreements. **Do not sign flat fee contracts!** Flat fee medicine, also knows as "capitation" must be avoided if at all possible. It is very difficult to make money under a capitated contract. It can be done, but it is for experienced people only and it is far beyond the scope of this book. Many a group went under because of capitated contracts! Do not repeat that mistake.

What is wrong with "flat fee medicine", i.e., capitated contracts?

Since these were once so common, it is worth examining why you should avoid them. The principle of capitation is this: the insurance pays a flat fee to the doctor, who in turn is obligated to see the patients no matter how often they come in. In essence, the insurance shifts the financial risk to the doctor. It is very difficult to determine a priori whether the capitated payments will cover the costs. Under capitated contracts, doctors make money if they keep the patients out of the office. Therefore, the doctor's incentive is to see the capitated patients as rarely as possible. However, the patients want to come in as often as possible, since it costs them a copay and nothing else. This is a misalignment of financial interests and leads to friction. You know you don't get paid, so you will try to keep the patients out, for example by dealing with minor illness on the phone, rather than bringing the patients in. But, guess what? The patients will come in no matter how hard you try to keep them out. The more they come in, the more costs they generate for the doctor. Soon a point is reached where the capitated payments no longer cover the costs and the doctor works for free. The final outcome is an irritated patient and an irritated doctor. In contrast, under fee-for-service agreements you get paid for each visit. Your incentive is to see them as often as possible, because you get paid for each encounter. Therefore you make yourself available, and you eliminate any hoops for the patient to jump through. You wind up with a happy patient, who will recommend you to his neighbor saying, "My doctor is always available!".

Often you hear this on capitation: "I understand the misalignment thing, but at least I get a check every month, it is like being on salary". Cool, you get a check, but does it cover your expenses? Doctors who talk like that don't understand of how expenses are generated, how much they are (in dollars) and therefore how much the capitation checks should be to cover them. Oh, by the way, covering expenses in not enough. You also need to make a profit!

How much should my pay be anyway?

Aaaahhh, now the fun stuff!
To answer this question, we need to discuss **your fees** first.

Setting your fees

Before you see patients you will need to set your fees first. There is a complicated way to do this and an easy one.

- **The complicated way**: you pick a dollar amount per Relative Value Unit and you multiply this amount by the number of units for each code. This assumes working knowledge of the Relative Value Units. This stuff is very dull and I do not recommend this course of action. For the beginner it is much too much work and if you make mistakes you complicate your life even more. Instead use the easy way described below.
- **The easy way**: you take the Medicare fees and double them, or better, multiply them by 2.5! That is you charge 2 – 2.5 times as much as Medicare pays. The Medicare reimbursement schedule is easily obtained from Medicare. It is called The Disclosure Statement for the state where you practice.

PEARL OF WISDOM

Here is some priceless advice: **you want to be expensive!** You must make sure your fees are higher than any insurance would ever want to pay you! I'm very serious, this is not flip stuff meant to be funny. It is very important. The reason is this: most of your contracts will say that you will be paid the lesser of your fees or an amount determined by the insurance. This amount may be the insurance's own determination, in which case it will be called "The Insurance X fee schedule". Or, it will be a percentage of Medicare payment. If you are lucky, it will be more than Medicare, for example 105%. The trick is to set your unit fees so high, that your fees will be far in excess of whatever any insurance would be willing to pay and also far in excess of Medicare reimbursement. The reason is precisely because the contract says it will pay "the lesser of…your fees or their reimbursement schedule". You don't want your fees to be "the lesser of…". Got it?

Please do not confuse what you charge with what you will pocket. These are very different numbers. You will rarely (if ever!) get paid what you charge. What you charge is "funny money". Only what you get paid is "real money". The reimbursement will vary from insurance to insurance. It will also vary over time. And since we are on the subject: often you hear doctors talk about the "percent reimbursement". This sounds like advanced business talk, when in fact it is utterly irrelevant! Consider this: the percent you get paid is a function of your fees. A doc who has high fees (relative to what he gets paid by the insurance plans) will have low reimbursement percentage, while a cheaper doctor may have higher reimbursement percentage. However, lo and behold, the guy with low percentage may very well wind up with more money if he sets his fees high and negotiates good reimbursement. Therefore talking about "percent reimbursement" may sound like expert talk, good for impressing clueless souls at happy hour. But in reality it is a useless number. You can change it instantly up or down simply by lowering or increasing your charges. You cannot even use it to track income over time, because, even if you leave your fees unchanged, the insurances change reimbursement all the time, thereby changing the infamous "percent reimbursement". Therefore, from now on, whenever you hear a doc telling you, his chest swelling with pride, that he gets "90 cents on the dollar", chuckle to yourself and regurgitate what you learned above. I guarantee you will impress (and deflate!) the fellow for good.

If you are looking for a measure of how your billings are doing, you need to track the distribution of the accounts receivable, not the "percent reimbursement". This will be discussed in future chapters.

Discounts

One more thing on fees! Every once in a while, you will have a patient who wants to pay cash for your services. Such patients are to be treasured, as they are rare! The problem is, you set your fees so high, it will scare Bill Gates away! What to do? The answer is, you set a different fee schedule for your cash paying patients. All billing software allows you to use more than one fee schedule. If you charge 2.5 x Medicare to insurances, charge 1.25 x Medicare for your cash paying patients. When cash paying Mr. Rare comes calling, say: "Normally I charge prices that would give you a heart attack, but for cash paying patients I give a X% discount". Everybody loves a discount.

WARNING: POTENTIAL LEGAL TROUBLE AHEAD!!

Pitfalls to avoid!

Your fees must be consistent. That means, you charge **ALL** insurances the same fees (let's say 2.5 x Medicare) and you charge **ALL** cash paying patients the same too (let's say 1.25 x Medicare). You cannot play favorites. You cannot give different discounts to different people willy-nilly. Be especially careful about varying your fees from insurance to insurance. To my knowledge it is illegal. The Feds (read Medicare) are particularly itchy about being charged a higher fee than commercial plans. Your lowest fees should never be less than Medicare.

Theoretically, you can have as many fee schedules as you want; for example you can give a 75% discount to cash paying patients and 80% to members of your golf club. However, for practical reasons, you want to keep is simple. I think having a single fee schedule for everybody with an x% discount for cash paying patients is about as complex as you want to be.

Back to the original question of how much is good reimbursement and what should you shoot for in your negotiations. What is "good pay" for a doctor in private practice these days? It depends where you practice! In rural areas, where doctors are scarce, reimbursement will be higher. In metro areas, choke-full with docs, you will have to make do with less. Like it or not, Medicare sets the standard. **In my opinion, if an insurance offers you more than Medicare, take it. If not, negotiate!** Of course, you should never hesitate to ask for more, even if you were offered exceptionally good reimbursement, but be realistic! You are not likely to get 200% Medicare.

Insurance products

You have products (the advice you give to patients and procedures you perform), so do insurances. Health insurance products include:

- **HMO**, which stands for Health Maintenance Organization. This product traditionally requires a patient to register with a primary care provider. The patient must see the PCP first, even if he knows he ultimately needs to be treated by a specialist. The patient cannot go to a specialist directly. Instead, the PCP needs to see him first and issue a referral. Hence the PCP is known as a "gate keeper". The idea is that expensive visits to specialists would be curbed, if you make the patient see the PCP first. The unspoken directive to the PCP is to treat everything he can possibly treat and avoid sending the patients to the specialists, which generates higher costs for the insurances. Nowadays this formerly iron clad directive has been softened considerably. Newer HMO products sometimes don't even require registration with a PCP any longer. It is beyond the scope of this book to go into all details of the HMO kingdom. All you need to know is that some of your patients will be enrolled in this type of product and therefore may very well require a referral from the PCP in order to see a specialist.

- **PPO**, which stands for Preferred Provider Organization. This product does not require a PCP. Patients can go directly to a specialist, if needed. No referral is necessary. Many patients like it because it frees them from the gate-keeper. It is also often cheaper than the HMO, because it has a deductible. This is how it works: an insurance negotiates discounts with a large number of doctors, who then become the "preferred providers". Patients who go to these preferred docs pay less than if they go to non-contracted doctors. It is in your interest to become part of PPOs because they give you access to large number of patients. Again, just like with the HMO, the subject is more complex than I can describe here.

- **Indemnity plans:** you'll love these! This is "classic" health insurance. The patient pays his premiums (which are high!) and has the freedom to go to any doctor he wants. Many times there are no restrictions at all. Medicare works like that. But there is a catch! In many instances the doctor has to accept whatever reimbursement the insurance pays. This reimbursement can be high or low. Many times it is not negotiable. For example: Medicare patients are free to go to any doctor willing to see them, but the reimbursement is not negotiable, the doctor has to accept Medicare fees. There are varieties of this product too, but for now, that's all you need to know.

- **IPAs**, which stands for Independent Physician Association. This is not a "true" insurance product, but I include it here since it is a close relative of the PPO. In essence, this is a reverse PPO. Doctors get together as a group and contract with various insurances. Joining an IPA can be a very good idea, because often they contract with many small plans, which would be too much work for an individual doctor. The disadvantage is that by joining the IPA you accept whatever reimbursement the IPA leadership negotiated with the insurances. This could be high or low, you need to look at the numbers to decide. You can join as many IPAs as you want. Note that by becoming a member of an IPA you do not join a group practice, but only a loose association consisting of many other doctors, some solo practitioners, some group practices.

PEARL OF WISDOM

No matter what insurance product you are dealing with, **always seek fee-for-service contracts.** Many times in the past HMO patients automatically came with capitated contracts. Not so any more. Whether the patient bought an HMO, PPO or whatever product, your contracts with his insurance must be fee-for-service. That way, the only difference to you is the technical handling of the patients: those on an HMO may need referrals to specialists, other may not. But **your financial incentive remains the same across all insurance products,** namely the more patients you have and the more you see them, the more money you make! Easy to remember, easy to apply. **The biggest mistake you can make is signing a mix of capitated and fee-for-service contracts. Remember, the capitated patients need to be kept out of your practice for you to make money. The others need to be brought in. It is impossible for your staff to remember which is which and act accordingly. CONSEQUENTLY, DO NOT SIGN CAPITATED CONTRACTS. PERIOD.**

Insurances to love, insurances to avoid

You should love all plans that pay a lot and quickly. To find out which is which, the beginner must talk at length with doctors already in practice in his area. These doctors will tell you how good the insurances are in their daily dealings with them. If you hear that an insurance is a pain, avoid it. This is especially true if the insurance is known to delay payments. Delayed payments are very expensive to you. This will be dealt with in the chapter on billings.

Tricks of the trade

Negotiating contracts with insurances requires some experience, but not that much. After all, in my view, the only thing worth negotiating for is higher reimbursement. You cannot learn how to negotiate from books. You need to jump into the fray and learn from your own experience. If you want some basic knowledge about negotiating, read

Negotiating for dummies by Michael C. Donaldson & Mimi Donaldson
Publisher: Hungry Minds (from the "for dummies" series)
ISBN: 1-56884-867-6

This is a very good introduction to the subject. But it is very much like learning how to listen to the heart by listening to tapes. It will give you an idea, but if you want to be good, you need to listen to the beating hearts of actual patients.

Some insurances are easy to deal with, others employ a **variety of tricks:**

- **Not showing you the fee schedule**. This is a classic and you are very likely to run into a situation like that. Here is how it works: the insurance sends you a contract, which says you will get paid as described in "Attachment X". Attachment X says you will get paid according to the insurance's own fee schedule, but the fee schedule itself is not attached.

What to do about it:

Stop the negotiation right there. Say you must have the fee schedule before you proceed. The insurance will say the fee schedule is proprietary information and you don't have a right to see it because you are not a contracted doctor. Duuuuh! This is like saying to a potential employee, "I'm not gonna tell you how much you'll get paid until you've worked here a month or so". It is completely unacceptable. You need to state very firmly that you must have the fee schedule. If they provide an incomplete one, insists again they give you all the numbers. Often they will give you a "sample" schedule of 50-odd codes. Of course, they will have chosen for this "sample" only their better paying codes. The "sample" in simply not enough to make a decision. You must see the whole thing. In my experience, insurances reluctant to show you their fees have lousy reimbursement. After all, insurances know how much the competition pays. If their respective pay were good, they would send it to you express mail and lined in red!

- **Making you sign a contract that covers all their products** (HMOs, PPO, worker's compensation, Medicare risk, etc.), when you only want a contract with one product.

What to do about it:

This is a judgment call. If you really want that product, if it is a high paying PPO for example, you may have to swallow the other stuff too. But it is worth making noise and insisting that you are offered a single product. Alternatively, you can say you will sign a contract covering all products, as long as you can cancel individual products later on. That way, after a time, you can cancel the lower paying products and keep the one with good reimbursement.

- Including a paragraph that says the **insurance reserves the right to change your coding**, rebundle, deny and change your reimbursement any time it pleases.

What to do about it:

This is advanced stuff. As a beginner, as a guy who simply wants to get started, I would not worry about it. However, ideally you should not sign such a thing. You should insist that they give you advanced notice of reimbursement policy changes. In my experience, this point is particularly hard to negotiate, because insurances use downcoding routinely to save money. If you are new to private practice I would not worry about this particular issue. Later on, when you have a booming practice and you notice an insurance downcodes your bills often, you can always tell them to get stuffed.

PEARL OF WISDOM

If you are located in an area where doctors are sparse, like Boondocks, New Mexico, the market forces are in your favor. Remember, **the thing that is rare is dear**. This applies to doctors too. If you are willing to live in an underserved area (read "The Sticks"), you are a rare commodity and therefore insurances will have to pay more for your services. If you want to live in a metropolitan area, you'll be just another doc in an ocean of docs. Your pay and your bargaining power will be reduced. In fact, if you are **in a metro area, your only "hold" over an insurance is your willingness to walk away from the negotiation.** You can certainly do that. The insurance won't give a hoot because they can easily replace you and you are left on the outside looking in. It is important to remember this. Don't get into a shouting match with an insurance that has plenty of docs on their panels. It will only raise your blood pressure. If you believe the contract is bad and the insurance will not improve the offer, walk away and save on blood pressure pills. Remember, the guy you are dealing with, who negotiates on behalf of the insurance, is just another employee on a steady salary. He could not care less about your irritations!

Chapter 5: LOCATION, RENT, PERSONNEL

Motto: Teamwork is when everybody does what I tell them.

Location

You can philosophize a lot about location, but if you want to reduce the issue to its essence, you have two choices:

- **You go where the patients are,** or
- **You go where the doctors (already) are.**

Where are the patients? Think **crowded areas** with high traffic, such as malls, strip malls and large office buildings. I even saw a medical clinic in an airport terminal. Something like "Fly to Vegas and get your air sickness pills too".

Why would you want to put your practice there? In a word: **convenience**. It is easier for your patients to do their shopping and get their Viagra prescription at the same time.

Where are the doctors? In **medical buildings**!

Why would you want to live there?

- The rent may very well be lower than at the mall.
- The landlord may have experience setting up a doctor's office.
- You are among colleagues with whom you can arrange for referrals and cross coverage.
- The building may be near the hospital where you admit (This is irrelevant if you are an outpatient-only doc).

PEARL OF WISDOM

Remember, you don't get paid for travel time. **If you're going to admit your own patients, you have no choice but to be near the hospital or even on the hospital campus.** This will be more expensive than a medical building somewhere in town, but well worth it, in my judgment!

Remember also that the **location determines the patient mix you will see.** If you only want Lexus driving yuppies for patients, don't go to the ghetto!

Incidentally, the neighborhoods where the yuppies live are very likely choke-full with doctors already.

What is the best way to find a good office location?

- Take your time, especially if you are new to town. Talk to all doctors you know about why they practice at that particular location. Their insight will be very useful.
- Doctors already in practice will guide you to their landlord and tell you how well they fared with that particular landlord.
- Thoroughly look over any medical building you are considering. Be especially careful to **observe what kind of patients come and go**. Spend some time in the lobby and look at the faces. Those are your future patients. Would you do their pap smears? If not, keep looking!
- There are companies that specialize in finding office space. These people know the market and can help you find what you need. This can save you a lot of driving around looking at office buildings, or searching through newspaper ads.

Rental contracts

The rent is almost always indicated in **dollars/square foot/year**. This is a weird way of pricing rent and it takes some getting used to. For example, an office may cost $ 18/sq.foot/year, meaning that if the office is 900 sq. feet, it will cost you $ 18 x 900/ year, or $1350/month.

Things to know about **rental contracts**:

- **Rent varies greatly from neighborhood to neighborhood.** Obviously, the more expensive a neighborhood, the more rent you can expect to pay.
- **Rent varies greatly from time to time.** Office space is a commodity, subject to market forces. If developers build a lot of office space in an area, the price will likely go down. However, when the economy is booming and most office space is already rented, prices will go up. There is so much fluctuation in prices, that I cannot give you a benchmark for what is "cheap" or what is "expensive" rent.
- **Rent is higher on a hospital campus, than a mile away**. However, if you are an admitting doctor, it is well worth paying more, if it allows you to walk from the hospital to your office. If you are an outpatient doc only, there is no need to be near a hospital.
- **Rent can be all inclusive,** which means it includes utilities and

cleaning.

- It can be **rent + extras.** The advantage of the latter is that you have some control over the cost of utilities. For example, you can set the air conditioning to a higher setting to save on electricity costs.
- Almost all rental contracts contain an **adjustment for inflation.** This means, each year the rent will go up by an amount approximately equal to the inflation rate. I find this particularly irritating, because doctors' reimbursement is rarely adjusted for inflation. However, very likely it is something you'll have to live with.
- **Almost all rental contracts are for several** years. You are not likely to find a landlord willing to rent month-to-month. The reason is the landlord wants to have a steady stream of income that he can rely on for years to come.
- Almost all rental contracts will require you to buy "**banana peel insurance**", in case patients get injured wile visiting your practice and sue you for it. This is not to be confused with malpractice insurance. It is much cheaper.
- Almost all rental contracts allow you to **sublease** to another doctor.

Things to try to get out of a landlord:

- **Renovate the office** to your specification before you move in. This should be at the landlord's expense. But please understand that there is no free lunch. Although on the face of it the landlord pays for the renovation, the money comes from you, since you pay the rent. When a landlord pays for the upgrades, be prepared to sign a longer lease. After all, the landlord wants to recover his expense. You may want to pay for the upgrades yourself if you want a short term contract. However, doing the upgrades assumes you know a good contractor. They are very, very hard to find.
- Try to **keep the duration of the contract as short as possible**, especially if you are in period of high prices. This will give you an opportunity to renegotiate a lower rent when you contract expires. Of course, this can backfire, since rent may very well go higher still!
- Try to get a **discount for the first 6 months** or so. Argue that you are new in practice and your income will be low in the beginning.
- Keep in mind that **the more concessions you squeeze out of a landlord, the longer the rental contract will be.** After all, if he gives you some discount upfront, he will want to know that you'll stay long enough to make-up for these initial expenses.

Hiring personnel

Let's be blunt, nobody really likes/wants to work! It is my conviction that human beings need to feel the tip of a boot in the crack of their asses to move. The tip of the boot can be different things to different people. Nevertheless, it is a requirement. It could be a boss breathing down their necks, or fear of hunger, of losing their houses, of not being able to go on vacation. Or it could be ambition, desire for power, glory, material goods. In other words, outside motivation is needed for us to work.

Let's be blunt again; **the role of the employee is to make you money**! Enough money to pay him and have a little left over for yourself.

PEARL OF WISDOM

The **cardinal principle** of all hiring decisions is this:

HIRE THE ATTITUDE, PROVIDE THE TRAINING!

What does this mean? The ideal employee is someone who has good knowledge of the job, has experience and a **good attitude.** Such an employee can slip into the job without requiring much training. However, such employees are very rare. More likely you will have to provide quite a bit of training to anyone you hire. What matters more than prior experience is a good attitude. If the attitude stinks, don't hire the guy. There are no exceptions to this. If you made the mistake of hiring such a person in the first place, get rid of him ASAP! Such an employee is not worth the money, no matter how knowledgeable and experienced he may be. Why? Because such people are impossible to manage and because bad attitude is known to spread to other employees. Yes, a bad apple spoils the whole cart.

How do you know bad attitude? It is hard to describe, but you'll know it when you see it.

Examples of **good attitude**:

- Dear boss, I never used a computer before, but I know it is important for the job. I'm willing to learn. Look, I already picked out a computer course at a community college. It is in the evening. I'm willing to sacrifice family time in order to attend this course, if you pay the tuition.
- Dear boss, I see you're tired and had a long day. Don't worry, I will stay late if needed and help you get through this long list of pa-

tients. Of course, I expect you to pay me overtime.
- Dear boss, while you were at lunch a patient with asthma came in. Instead of calling you back urgently, I placed the patient in a quiet and comfortable exam room, administered oxygen and an SVN and he is now breathing easier.

Et cetera! You get the picture. Notice that good attitude has nothing to do with the employee's knowledge or experience. The person could be the world's premier expert on something and still disqualify himself from working in your office by virtue of his bad attitude.

Examples of **bad attitude:**

- Giving the boss things to do! This is a classic, because it shows not only an unwillingness to solve problems, but also insubordination.
- Picking fights with other employees.
- Behaving like he is the boss over other employees who in fact are of equal rank.
- Politicians, backstabbers, people who cannot take their heads out of your ass, slimy, greasy personalities.
- Disloyal people who betray a trust placed in them.

And so on! **Bad attitude** is such a problem because it **is incurable.** I believe human personality is completely formed by the time you are in your mid-twenties. After that, in cannot be modified. No matter what motivational courses you send him to, no matter how much patience you show, the person with bad attitude remains a problem. Very likely he lacks any insight. And that is the reason why he must go.

Incidentally, I also believe very strongly you should never work for a boss with a bad attitude! If you find yourself in such a job, quit immediately. The problem boss is in my view just as incurable as the problem subordinate!

Don't misunderstand me. I'm not talking about someone who has a bad day, or even a bad three months. Everybody has ups and downs and everybody blows a fuse every once in a while. I am talking about a chronic issue, not a temporary one.

The ideal employee

Let's say you are looking for a biller. What should you look for in your candidates? Ideally:

- The candidate should have worked as a biller before and have enough knowledge and experience to start right away. Training should not be required, beyond explaining your computer system to him. After that it should be: "Here is the pile of bills for today, get them done".

- He should have deep understanding of the job and know how to deal with any quirks that invariably come up. For example, you billed for a procedure, but forgot to bill for the surgical tray and the anesthetic. A good biller should catch that and ask you to rectify it before sending it out.
- He should find ways to increase your revenue. Ideally, of course, you the boss, already have your practice set up in such a way as to maximize revenue. But don't be cute, there is always something new to learn, even for you. For example, a good biller may point out that a second procedure you did was performed in the global period. You should have waited another week, so you can get paid for the second procedure too.
- Above all, he should have good attitude (see above).

The problem with the ideal employees

- They are so rare that it is unrealistic to hope to fill your practice with such people.
- They rarely appear on the open job market. Such people, should they want to switch jobs, can find a new employer rather quickly, through word of mouth. "What, Mr. Genius is looking for a job? Of course I'll hire him!" Don't expect such a candidate to show up at your door step after you placed an advertisement in the paper. These people do not need to look in the paper to find employment.
- They are expensive. Very expensive. They know their worth and will not settle for less. After all, a biller like the one describe above, could very well start his own billing company. Why should he work for you?
- In an economic downturn they are the last ones to lose their jobs (if they loose them at all!) and the first ones to be hired when the economy improves.
- If you should lucky enough to have hired such an employee, see that you keep him! Think high salary and perks.

Since you're not likely to find many ideal employees, you must learn to settle for less. That is why a good attitude is so important. When you find someone with good attitude, you can teach him how to do the job. Prior experience becomes much less important. If the guy is willing to learn, teach him! This takes time, but it is time well spent. In fact, with proper training and enough longevity in your practice, the beginner you hired may very well metamorphose into an ideal employee. Now you see my point: **HIRE THE ATTITUDE, PROVIDE THE TRAINING!**

People management

If you go to a library and read all the books on people management you will notice a common denominator: **there are no books on how to manage bad employees!** The reason is because it cannot be done. All teaching material on people management assumes that your employees **want to be managed!** This means that you have already weeded out all bad apples and are now left with a work force that actually wants to work! I cannot say it often enough; get rid of the problem children immediately. Otherwise you will have chaos in the practice.

How do you manage your employees on a day-to-day basis? There are many books on the subject and I read a few of them. For a budding boss the best books are:

The supervisor's book of lists by George T. Fuller
Publisher: Prentice Hall ISBN: 0-13-122771-8

By looking at these lists, you gather insight into the process of management itself. It is more than just a book on listing things and prioritizing, because it conveys basic knowledge too.

Managing for dummies by Bob Nelson & Peter Economy
Publisher: IDG books (the "for dummies" series of books)
ISBN: 1-56884-858-7

This is a very good 101 course in management. Since you are not looking at being the next CEO of Megamedicine, Inc., this book is all you need to manage your employees.

Practical examples on people management

I don't want to repeat here what you can read in other books, such as the ones listed above. Instead, let's discuss some "cases".

Example 1: A "temporary" pay raise becomes permanent.

A medical practice loses an important employee who moves out of state for personal reasons. While a new employee is recruited, one of the remaining employees is asked to pitch in temporarily and shoulder additional responsibilities. As an "incentive" he will receive a higher salary while he does the extra work, but will drop back to his original pay once the position is filled. He agrees and signs a letter saying he understands the higher pay is temporary.

The answer

Guess how this plays out? Once a new hire is found, he won't hear anything about going back to his original pay. Instead, he wants to keep his higher salary, although his workload is now back to normal. When he is reminded of his signed agreement, he reluctantly gives in, but a few months later quits.

The take home lesson

Don't give temporary pay increases! No matter how clear the agreement, temporary is perceived to be permanent. Instead, give time-off, movie tickets, flowers, gift certificates, or pats on the back.

Example 2: Flexible hours, flexible boss, flexible employee.

A practice has regular hours of operation 8 – 17. The receptionist (who is doing a very good job) has a son who starts school in a month. He will have to drop him off at school at 8:00 and pick him up at 17:00; he can come in at 8:30 and must leave by 16:30. He wants to know if he could compensate for his decreased presence by "working through lunch", thereby keeping the total number of working hours to 40 a week.

The answer

"Working through lunch" or "staying late" to make up for lost time is a very common request. However, I do not think it is a good idea. It may be illegal too, but don't quote me on that. From a practical stand point, it is a very bad idea to make such concessions to employees. Instead, the employee was offered the following deal: the practice is willing to be flexible on his work hours is he is willing to be flexible on his salary. In English this means that he would work an hour a day less, but receive an hour a day less pay. It is a fair deal. The practice understands that parents need flexible work hours, but cannot allow him to work 35 hour weeks and keep the same salary. That would play very badly with the other employees, who would still be required to work 40 hour weeks to get their full salaries. Fortunately, the receptionist agrees. This confirms the good impression his employer had of him. He shows maturity by understanding that he cannot expect something for nothing.

The take home message

I believe that flexible hours are needed when you have employees with children in school. The school dictates not only when such employees can work, but also when they must take vacations. Since you, the doctor/owner of the practice can set your own hours of operation, it should be possible to accommodate requests for flexible hours from employees. I would go even further than that. If you have a key employee whom you don't want to lose, I would advise you to modify the hours of operation of the practice to accommodate this very important employee. However, nobody should expect to work less and get paid the same. That is unreasonable and you should never agree to that.

Example 3: You hired the wrong guy.

A practice hires a new employee, who appears very friendly during his interview. After a few weeks on the job, there are good things to report and bad ones. On the good side, the employee could not be more pleasant, is liked by the boss and handles patients very well. On the negative side, it becomes increasingly clear that the employee has great difficulty reading and writing. Patient names are misspelled in the computer, various notes in the chart are impossible to read because of bad grammar, he cannot follow written instructions. The painful truth emerges: the employee is functionally illiterate.

The answer

There is nothing to be done! The practice has a 3 months probationary period for all new hires. It is clear that the employee will not pass. The employee understands this and quits. The departure is friendly, which makes it easier on all involved, because it avoids a "firing".

The take home message

No matter how well a candidate interviews, there can be surprises later on. In this case, the practice could not have done anything. After all, reading and writing are basic skills that cannot be taught on the job.

Example 4: Blackmail!

A practice has three employees. Two have been working there for many years, the third was hired only eight months ago. One of the old employees quits unexpectedly and leaves the practice short handed. Seizing the moment, the new hire states that he wants more pay, or he, too, will quit. Evidently, the practice has no choice but to give in. After all, if he also departs, it will leave the doctor with only 1 employee, making it impossible to run the practice. Or so he thinks!

The answer

This is blackmail in its chemically purest form. The rebellious employee must be fired on the spot.

The take home message

Any business depends on its employees. You owe it to them to be a good boss. They, in turn, owe you the same courtesy. It is completely out of line for employees to ask for a pay hike before the first anniversary. It is even more so to say "or else!". A practice that gives in to this request opens the flood gates for similar requests. The practice has no choice but to fire this person and muddle through the shortage. This can be done by decreasing the hours of operation until new employees are hired.

Example 5: You get lucky!

A practice has three employees. One quits. Replacement is hard to find, because of low unemployment. Eventually, a new hire is found, but at 50% higher salary than the departing employee. The new employee is a very respectable person, with many qualities. However, he has little knowledge of medical stuff and requires a lot of training. The doctor has to spend time explaining even the most basic medical knowledge to the new hire. But guess what happens? The new employee has a good attitude, is well organized and quickly picks up new knowledge. After a year, he has taken over so many functions, that the practice can now operate with only two employees. Consequently, the work force can be reduced to two, realizing significant savings for the doctor.

The answer

This is proof positive that a good attitude is more important than experience. This practice got lucky. Initially it looked as if the personnel costs have gone up. On top of that, the doctor had to baby-sit the new employee on a daily basis. But, with time, it paid off.

The take home message

If you are lucky enough to have such an employee, see that you keep him. This is the "ideal employee" discussed above. Very likely he will expect very good pay and the doctor would be foolish not to give it to him!

The last word on managing your workforce: don't give them group health insurance!

In the US employers buy group health insurance and provide it to their workforce. For the workers this is a very important benefit. For the businesses it is a nightmare! How did American businesses get into this mess? After all, to my knowledge, the US is unique in this respect. No other country knows this system of health insurance! I heard that during the Second World War wages were frozen and businesses rewarded their employees with "benefits" instead of salary increases. Thus, the employer sponsored health insurance was born.

Group insurance allows participation irrespective of the worker's health status. Even the biggest train wrecks qualify. Costs are low for the employees, because most of the tab is picked up by the employer. Workers have come to view this as a true case of "something for nothing", i.e., insurance that does not cost them much. They don't understand that it does come out of their paychecks, however indirectly. After all, the money the boss spends on health insurance is money he will not pay out in salary! But the employers are not only burdened with the costs. They must go shopping for insurance, administer the plan for their workers and act as a "wailing wall" for the workers whenever they are dissatisfied with the insurance.

It is my conviction that as a doctor in private practice you must avoid this. Don't provide group health insurance for your employees! You will be under pressure to do so. When you interview prospective employees, one of the first questions they will ask will be about health insurance. Some will not even consider working for you if you don't offer group insurance. However, I strongly counsel you to remain steadfast. If you start buying group insurance for your employees you will spend countless hours administering this benefit, time that is not reimbursed. Instead, offer your employees an **alternative**: individual insurance.

Find an insurance broker whom your employees can contact. He will help them find a suitable plan. The employees will have to pass a medical test to get individual insurance. Unlike group plans, individual plans decline to insure applicants with certain medical conditions. After all, you don't insure a burning house. However, these plans are much cheaper than group insurance. You, the employer can offer to pick up some of the tab. For example, you can offer to pay $100 a month towards health insurance. Incidentally, this is tax free to the employee. The advantage of my suggestion is that it puts the burden of finding and maintaining insurance on the employees, <u>where it belongs</u>! The boss helps pay a portion of the premium, but the employees pick their own insurance. That way you are completely out of the loop whenever there are problems with the insurance. The employee picks it, the employee has to deal with it.

A final last word: the staff and your mail

It would seem logical to allow the staff to open the mail. After all a lot is junk! However, I strongly caution it against it: **DO NOT ALLOW THE STAFF TO OPEN YOUR MAIL.** No, I don't have an undiagnosed case of paranoia. Here are the reasons:

- **Modifications to contracts with health plans**. Most contracts say that the insurances are free to change the terms of the contract. All they need to do is mail you (registered/receipt) the proposed changes. If you don't respond within 30 days, they become effective. In my office I used to let the staff open the mail until a major problem happened. One of our insurances sent such a contract modification. It said they will no longer pay us according to the negotiated rates; instead the payments will be "updated" to their latest fee schedule. Ummmmhh! Sounds fishy. The "update" was in fact a major drop in reimbursement! The receptionist, who happened to be at the desk when the mail arrived signed for the letter, opened it, thought it was junk and threw it in the recycle bin. I happened to find it when I emptied the recycle bin a few days later. The letter caught my eye entirely by accident! That was the last day staff were allowed to open mail. Some things are just too complicated for secretaries and receptionists to deal with. If I had not found the letter, the 30 days allowed for my response would have passes and we would have ended up with lower reimbursement!
- **You get sued.** When a lawsuit is served, you certainly don't want your staff to know it! Therefore, don't let them open the mail. Especially mail from lawyers.
- **You get investigated by the medical board.** Again, employees must not know about this.
- **Temptation, temptation!** Let's face it: your employees make a lot less money than you do! Human nature being what it is some will not resist the temptation to give themselves "bonuses" by diverting some of the insurance payments to themselves. The best strategy is for the insurance payments to go to a different address, for example to your house or a post office box. More about this in the chapter on billings.
- **Lab results.** Most of the time you can trust your staff to recognize an important test result and bring it to your attention accordingly.

However, remember, they are not doctors and may very well mis-interpret something. Is a renal oncocytoma good news or bad news for the patient? Don't let your receptionist decide!

Chapter 6: COMPUTERIZED RECORDS AND BILLING

Motto: Where we are, nothing works. But we can't be everywhere.

Computers and medical records

Traditionally, doctors dictated their notes, the dictations were transcribed (often off-site, by a transcription company), mailed back to the doctor, coded for billings and then put in their final resting place, i.e., the chart. **This is the most expensive and inefficient way to keep records imaginable.** Not only you pay the transcriptionist for work that you can do yourself, but often the note takes a week or more to find its way into the chart. If the patient comes back during this time and sees your partner, he will not have an up-to-date chart.

Since the patient encounter is not coded until the transcription comes back to the office, sending out the bill to the insurance is delayed unnecessarily for at least several days. On top of all this, the costs of this traditional method are very high, about $500/ month. Utter folly. You must do better than this!

The modern way to write and keep records: computerized records

The software

In the doctor's office computers are needed for a variety of functions. In this chapter I will deal with patient record keeping and billings. There are software packages that do records, but not billings, while others do billings but not patient notes and there are packages that do everything. Irrespective of what software you buy, please remember this very important warning:

The software industry (for the doctor's office) is in its early stages. Many of the software companies currently in business will not survive and will disappear. Let's say you bought a software package from a company that went out of business. Obviously, it can no longer provide technical support and upgrades. Instead of upgrades, you will be forced to buy new software from another company. Very likely, the new software will not read the files written by the old software. Just like QuickBooks will not read a Word file. This presents an insurmountable problem: **you cannot**

read your old patient notes, or you cannot access your old billings, or both.

To avoid this, I would strongly counsel you to:

- **Whatever software you buy, make sure its files can be read by other widely used programs, such as WordPad.** That way, if the software company goes out of business, you can still access your old files.
- **If that is not possible, strongly consider writing your notes using a simple, off-the-shelf program like Word or WordPerfect.** Word-processing has been around long enough to ensure that future programs will know how to read old files. Additionally, neither Microsoft, nor the makers of WordPerfect are likely to go out of business any time soon, leaving you without support or upgrades.
- **Unfortunately, there is no off-the-shelf billings software.** You have no choice by to buy a program from a company that may disappear in the future.
- **If you want to play it safe, use a word processor for your patient notes and a dedicated program for your billings, rather than a package that does everything.** That way, if the billings software becomes obsolete, you can at least access your patient notes.
- **Make sure the software runs on the Windows (or Mac) platform and does not require a specialized hardware system of its own.** Specialized hardware is very expensive and you double your risk of being left without support or upgrades: not only your software but also your hardware company might go out of business, leaving you <u>completely stranded.</u>

It is beyond the scope of this book to review software packages currently on the market. Besides, this field is evolving so rapidly that any software review would be out-of-date by the time you read this. If you want to see all software packages together in one place, the best place to see them on display is at the Annual Conference of the Whateveryourspecialtyis. They all have stands in the exhibit room. Instead, I will focus on a solution that will not leave you stranded: use Word for notes and a cheap billings program. Now let's talk about the necessary hardware.

The hardware

Let's say you are a solo practitioner with three employees. A receptionist, who sits at the **front desk**, a nurse, who has a **workstation in the patient area** and a biller, who also acts as "office manager" and who has his own **"billings" room.**

This is where your computer literacy pays off big time! Here is how to do it:

- When your landlord renovates the office, make sure you install computer networking cables for all relevant positions.
- Take a PC and place it on your desk. The only programs you need for your office are a word processor and a billing program (see below). Consequently, buy a garden variety computer and forget about the fancy stuff like expensive video and sound cards. Let's call this the "**main computer**". Hook-up to it an external hard drive, for all your data.
- Buy three more computers and place them on the respective desks of the receptionist, nurse and biller.
- Network these four computers together. That way, you can access the data from all workstations. You can accomplish this with a hub. Hubs are cheap. If you don't know what buttons to push to make all computers talk to each other, hire a geek to do so.
- Install all necessary software on all computers. However, make sure the data is stored on the external drive of the "main" computer located in your room. You don't want the data spread over several computers and fragmented.

PEARL OF WISDOM

Do not place your data on the C-drive of the main computer! Why? Because at the end of the day, you detach the external drive and lock it up for the night. That way, the cleaning crew who comes in after hours does not have access to your patient data. It is very important to realize that **your office is not empty after hours**. At the very least there will be a cleaning crew. The landlord may also do maintenance work that cannot be done during office hours because of noise or dust. Cleaning and maintenance crews are notorious for opening the door and keeping it open while they work. During this time, anybody can come in unnoticed and "relieve" you of your patient data by stealing the computer. You need to worry not only about **burglars,** but also about **disgruntled employees,** who may want to get back at you this way. Have a cabinet fitted with a special key (for example a Medeco lock that cannot be picked) and store the external hard drive in it at night. You and possibly one other trusted employee should be the only ones with a key to this cabinet. That way, you limit the access to this very important data. Remember, it is difficult to destroy or steal a large paper chart. But it is very easy to steal a computer. The best prevention is a locked cabinet. More about computer security later, but I think the best password protected system is worthless, if the entire computer can be stolen!

Additional hardware you will need:

- **A scanner**. Not all your records will be computerized. Sometimes you will receive records from other doctors, radiology readings and pathology reports that are written on paper. **Do not create a computerized record and a paper record for each patient. Instead, scan all paper records and keep only computerized records and no paper!** This is the modern way to keep medical records and the cheapest!
- **A DVD or CD burner**. New computers already have them, so it is not really "additional" hardware. At the end of each day, make a back-up of all the data stored on your external drive. Use a DVD-RW or a CD-RW disc for this, so you can use it more than once. Take the back-up disc home and back it up again on two more media, for example on two more external hard drives attached to your home computer. Note that you should not back it up on the C drive of your home computer, because it can be stolen too. **When you go on vacation, take the external hard drives and store them in a bank safe deposit box.** That way, if someone breaks into your house when you are gone, you don't loose any patient data.

Now you are up and running as far as your computer system is concerned.

PEARL OF WISDOM

Use hardware you can buy off-the-shelf in stores such as BestBuy. Do not use custom-made stuff. It is much, much more expensive and it can only be serviced by the people who made it. The computer system described above allows you to perform all record keeping and billings for your office. You don't need anything fancier, or more costly.

The wrong way to buy hardware for your office

There are scores of vendors selling "specialized" hardware systems for doctors' practices. Just like the software companies, you can see them if you go to the Annual Meeting of the American Society of Whateveryourspecialtyis. They all have stands in the exhibit room. The problems with these vendors are:

- **They are very, very expensive**. I have rarely seen anything below $ 8,000 and you can spend north of $ 15,000. What do you get for this money? The same thing you can build with off-the-shelf hardware! Please remember **anything you buy triples in price if it is**

labeled "for the medical office". A lousy desk that may cost $ 500 at OfficeMax, will set you back $ 2000 at the "medical office supply store". Same with computer systems.

- **They are all small vendors, in business since this morning.** You don't know if their products work with other vendor's hardware and software. The best office package does not help you if it does not work with the clearinghouse of your choice. In addition, as mentioned, you don't know if they are going to be in business tomorrow, when you will need service and upgrades.

Until big companies like Microsoft and Intuit come up with packages for the doctor's office, use exclusively off-the-shelf components. The big guys will be around the next day to provide service and upgrades. Remember, computer hardware for the doctor's office is at the stage of the Model-T Ford: cute for its time, but a long way from where it needs to be!

Computer security

All computerized systems have three enemies:

- Theft
- Accidental deletion of data
- Access of medical information by unauthorized persons

Here is how to deal with them:

Principles of data management

Keep is simple

As noted above, **all data must be kept in the same place**, i.e., on the external hard drive hooked up to the main computer. The other computers in the office allow access to the data via the network. But **do not use these computers for data storage.** When your receptionist registers a patient, the data generated will be saved on the external hard drive noted above and nowhere else. When your nurse has a telephone conversation with a patient and documents said conversation, again the data goes to the external hard drive.

Prevent theft

How is computer data stolen? If you store your data on the C drive of your computer, all data will disappear when the computer is stolen. To prevent this, **do not store the data on the C drive.** I cannot say this often enough: **buy an external hard drive and store the data on it! At night, lock**

up the external hard drive in a safe place. Have a cabinet fitted with a lock that cannot be picked and lock the hard drive inside it at night. That way, if a burglar comes in at night, he will have to pick not only the lock to your office, but also the lock to the cabinet. This lessens the chance of theft. The additional reason why you should lock the hard drive at night is what I said above: after hours your office is in fact open whenever the cleaners are at work. The cleaners are busy with their vacuums and will not notice if somebody sneaks in and steals your computers. If you lose your computers you're going to say some choice words. But if you lose the data you are toast!

Prevent the consequences of accidental deletion of data: BACK IT UP

Notice I did not say prevent the accidental deletion. Accidental deletion will happen no matter what measures you put in place. It happens at least three to four times a year in my office. Accidental deletion is not a disaster if you back up regularly. Here is how to do it:

- **Every day**, at the end of the business day, you back-up the data from your external hard drive to a DVD or CD. Notice I said **you! The job of backing up the data is the doctor's responsibility.** Do not ever, ever EVER dump this chore on your staff. Remember, it is **your** data, you are responsible for it, not your staff.
- Take the DVD or CD home and the back it up some more. I use 2 other external hard drives attached to my home computer. The reason I do not back it up on the C drive of my home computer is the same as for the office: I don't want to lose the data if the home computer should be stolen. When I go on vacation, I lock up the external drives in a safe deposit box at my bank.

If data is accidentally deleted, you pull out your DVD or CD and restore it immediately. If you notice the deletion immediately, you can restore the complete data immediately from your back-up. If you don't notice it immediately you will have to redo the work performed since the last back-up. In my experience, this is no big deal. Most employees remember what they did since the last back-up and will know what needs to be rewritten. That is why it is important to **back-up every day!**

PEARL OF WISDOM

The cardinal principle of data back-up is that **data must be stored in at least 2 different locations.** That way if your office burns down overnight, you still have the data at home. If your home gets ransacked while you are on vacation, you will not lose the data, because it is in the safe at the bank. Got it?

How to deal with accidental deletion that is not noticed immediately

This is in fact your biggest headache: an employee deletes a file and does not realize it! Don't worry, there is a cure for this too. Here is how to do it: when you take your data home and back it up on the external drives of your home computer, **do not overwrite the previous back-up. Instead, create a back-up file for each business day.** Your back-ups should look like this:

- Smith practice 09-09-2003
- Smith practice 09-10-2003
- Smith practice 09-11-2003
- Smith practice 09-12-2003
- Smith practice 09-13-2003 and so on.

Let's say 6 months later you notice that the file for patient XY is missing. It was deleted accidentally, but you don't know when. It could have been yesterday, it could have been 3 months ago. Panic? No way! You simply go back in time through your back-ups until you find it. Which brings me to another point:

How long do you keep backing-up?

I would advise you to keep at least 2 years' worth of daily back-ups. Will all that data fit on an external hard drive? Easily! My daily file is about 100 MB and a 100 GB external drive will hold 2 years' worth of data. If you don't have enough room, buy a bigger external hard drive!

PEARL OF WISDOM

Do not EVER use the Windows back-up feature! This program resides in "Accessories/System Tools". This program not only backs-up a file, but also compresses it. At least that is what I think it does. Good luck finding a program that can read the compressed file! It needs to be decompressed first and in all my years of using computers I have never found this to be a practical solution. Instead, use the "copy" and "paste" commands in Windows Explorer. This makes an exact copy of the original file, which can be read using the program that wrote it in the first place. For example, let's say you use Word to write your patient notes. Go to Windows Explorer and right-click on the file; click "copy", then right-click on your DVD or CD drive and click "paste". This copies the original Word file from its original location to the CD and does not change it at all. You can now access the CD and use the back-up file just like you use the original.

Windows XP Professional

The big deal about XP Professional as far as medical offices are concerned is that you can use its security features to protect access to folder/files. This should help prevent accidental deletion and unauthorized access (see below). It is beyond the scope of this course to go into the security features of XP Professional. But you can do it yourself: create some files and play with them on your computer and see how you can password-protect them or assign different levels of access to them. Please note that XP Home edition does not have all the security features of the Professional edition. It's the Professional you want for your office, or whatever successor it will have.

Unauthorized access

The new HIPPAA requirements state that you must take measures against unauthorized access of medical information. It is beyond the scope of this book to go into HIPAA, but by the time you start your own office, the HIPAA regulations will likely be familiar to you anyway.

Let's say you are an office with 3 employees as noted above: receptionist, nurse, and biller/manager. You must decide who should have access to what part of your electronic chart. Theoretically, the receptionist, whose job is to schedule patients and answer the phone, should not have access the medical information in the chart. The same theoretical consideration applies to the biller. However, this is a case where theory and practice collide! My personal experience shows that a small office like a solo practice should not layer access to the data. Many times a patient calls and asks the receptionist if he is due for a "physical". If the receptionist cannot access the medical information in the chart, the practice comes to a screeching halt. The receptionist must then find someone who has access to the information in order to answer the question. This is very impractical. I think a small office like the one described has no choice but to allow access to all data to all employees. Otherwise chaos ensues. However, I cannot make such a blanket recommendation to all small offices. There may be very good reasons for layering access. You need to make yourself familiar with the law and decide for yourself how to apply it.

The medical practice and the Internet

Don't use the Internet from a computer where patient data is stored. It can be stolen by hackers and you won't even know it! If you feel compelled to use the Internet in your office, **first disconnect your external hard drive where the patient data resides from your computer. Then and only then go online**. This is an additional reason why you should not keep your practice data on the C drive of a computer. I would also advise you to avoid fast Internet connections such as ISDN, cable or broadband in your office. Instead use a "slow-poke" telephone line. The reason is that a slow line is so slow, hackers will lose patience and go looking somewhere else.

At this stage, in my opinion, medical offices and the Internet don't mix! The reason is security. If hackers steal patient data from your office much damage will be done. In my opinion firewalls are an insufficient obstacle between patient data and hackers. I know I would not want my own medical information protected by a firewall and nothing else.

I believe in the future the Internet will play a big and very helpful role in medical billings. I think in the future clearinghouses will disappear and doctors will submit their bills directly to the insurances via secure Internet connections and websites. Insurance enrollment, eligibility and referrals will be checked online. To a certain extent this is already happening. But a lot of issues need to be addressed before every Joe Shmoe, MD should start doing it.

One last word on the Internet: **DO NOT ALLOW YOUR PERSONNEL TO USE THE INTERNET FROM THE OFFICE COMPUTERS.** The reason is they are not conversant with the issues of Internet security, such as data theft, cookies etc. Using the Internet is not a required job skill in a medical office in 2004. It may be in the future, but until then I would strictly forbid Internet usage by the staff. In my office, employees know that going online from an office computer is cause for immediate termination with cause. No excuses allowed.

PEARL OF WISDOM

Very likely you will need to train your personnel on all issues mentioned above. Very few candidates for jobs in your office will be computer literate. Take your time and train them well, because you want your staff to be conversant with your computer system. You don't want to be interrupted during a procedure because the receptionist cannot find a file, or panics because the file seems to have "vanished". This, of course, assumes **you, the doctor, know this stuff inside out. THIS IS PRECISELY THE REASON WHY YOU MUST BE COMPUTER LITERATE TO HAVE AN OFFICE.** I truly believe that computer illiterate doctors should learn computers first before opening their own shops.

The computerized medical record

You have a computer network in your office, you understand how it works and you are conversant with the principles of data management like back-up and security. Cool! But how is the data generated in the first place. Exactly how do you write notes?

As mentioned, the logical choice for writing your notes is a **word processor, like Word or Word Perfect.** After all, the entire content of a doctor's note is precisely that which a word processor handles best, namely text! I predict than in future there will be dedicated, cheap and user friendly software specifically written for the medical office. Until then, go back to using Word! Take my word for it!

Generic notes

Many patient encounters cover standard issues or diseases that are seen frequently, such as school physicals, colds, admissions for pneumonia, operative reports for elective surgeries, back pain and migraines. You should write generic notes for all these encounters. When you have a patient that fits, "copy" and "paste" the generic note into the chart, then modify the things that need to be changed to fit a particular patient. In my opinion, the "copy" and "paste" commands are the most useful features ever created for a word processor.

Incidentally, if you bought a dedicated record keeping software package, it will come with prewritten generic notes for your specialty. Not only that, but it will have prewritten notes for each evaluation and management level. Let's say you just saw a patient with cholecystitis and decided to recommend surgery. The software will have the appropriate e/m encounter written for a level 5 code. You will not need to write the entire note every time you see a patient with a routine problem. All you do is pick the appropriate note from a list of prewritten notes. The advantages include:

- Your documentation will be up-to-date with the most recent coding requirements.
- You can use the note as a cheat-sheet to ensure you covered all relevant areas if you have a complex patient. For example, I use my generic notes to remind myself to cover all that needs to be covered for a diabetic visit.
- You cover your ass as well as you can possibly cover it, because all your notes are consistent and complete.
- You prescriptions are prewritten too. You don't need to rewrite

the entire 20-meds list every time a gomer comes in for refills. You simply print what you have already written before.

Practical examples of how to use a generic note

I don't have custom-made software. I use Word. I have a folder called "Generics" which has 40-odd generic notes to fit many standard situations. Here is the one for allergic rhinitis:

h/o running, itchy nose, night time post-nasal drip and stuffiness, running itchy eyes; no wheezing or asthma.

o: nad a&o; nose is running
-oropharynx: normal except post-nasal drip
-neck: supple, no adenopathy
-nares: irritated, but otherwise ok
-eyes: normal

a/p:

1. Allergic rhinitis:

-avoid exposure to allergens (if known and possible)
-use CTM 4m po bid (otc) and
-Allegra 60mg po bid # 1month; 2 refills
-Claritin 10mg po qd #1 month; 2 refills
-Vancenase-AQ 2 puffs in each nostril qd #1; 2 refills
-Nasacort AQ 2 puffs in each nostril qd #1; 2 refills
-MOA, s/e discussed in detail, if sedation becomes a problem, will call me back; pt understands both drugs need to be used daily to get a benefit, prn use is not likely to work.

f/u 2 mos

Let's say a patient with this disease comes to see me. I copy the generic note into that patient's Word chart and modify it accordingly. Let's say this patient is a 30 y/o man who was troubled by this disease for 3 years and had not done anything about it so far. Let's also say that I recommended Chlortrimeton (CTM) for treatment, but did not recommend any of the other treatments mentioned in the generic chart. The final note will look like this:

30 y/o m with 3 yr h/o running, itchy nose, night time post-nasal drip and stuffiness, running itchy eyes; no wheezing or asthma.

o: nad a&o; nose is running
-oropharynx: normal except post-nasal drip
-neck: supple, no adenopathy
-nares: irritated, but otherwise ok
-eyes: normal

a/p:

1. Allergic rhinitis:

-avoid exposure to allergens (if known and possible)
-use CTM 4m po bid (otc)
-MOA, s/e discussed in detail, if sedation becomes a problem, will call me back;
f/u 2 mos

Notice I added the words "**30 y/o m with 3 yr**" at the beginning of the note, and I deleted the words

"**-Allegra 60mg po bid # 1month; 2 refills
-Claritin 10mg po qd #1 month; 2 refills
-Vancenase-AQ 2 puffs in each nostril qd #1; 2 refills
-Nasacort AQ 2 puffs in each nostril qd #1; 2 refills**"
pt understands both drugs need to be used daily to get a benefit, prn use is not likely to work."

because I did not recommend any of those medicines at this time. Writing this note and saving it to disc takes no time at all. And, of course, I use the patient's own name to name his file.

Generic notes and coding

When you first write your generic notes, **attach the code to them**. You know what issues need to be covered in order to make an evaluation and management encounter a level 2, 3, 4, or 5. Include these elements accordingly. That way you don't need to look-up the code for each of your notes.

The ultra-modern way of writing notes

In addition to the computer system described above, the ultra-modern doctor carries a Palm Pilot or equivalent with him to the patient room. In this Palm computer you store all the patient data. That way you have it available when you talk to the patient and you can write your note, or adapt a generic note while in the room with the patient. At the end of the day, you download all the notes you have written onto the external drive and back-up the file as described above. In addition, you carry the Palm thing with you when on call. It's like having all your patient notes in your pocket. If a patient calls you, all his data is available, such as medicines he is taking, when he saw you last and what you discussed with him. You can make notes after you talk to the patient and later download them into your office computer system.

Billings

PEARL OF WISDOM

Do not ever outsource the billings! Billings must be done in house. Repeat after me: **BILLINGS MUST BE DONE IN YOUR OWN OFFICE!** Directly under your nose. Closely supervised by you. You will likely hire an employee to do the billings, a biller. However, the biggest expert on billings in your office needs to be...YOU!

The theory behind farming out billings

I'm going to say this from the start, it is an invalid theory! Many doctors say they want to save money on personnel and software by farming out the billings. NEVER do that. Money spent doing billings in house is money well spent.

Outsourcing works like this: a person with knowledge billings starts a "billings company" of his own, often in his own house. Ideally this should be a professional, trained coder and biller, who has many years experience under his belt. He will tell you to send him your charges and he will do the rest. The "rest" in this case consists of sending out the bills, either electronically or by mail, as the case may be. The insurances will then issue their payments and the biller will be paid a percentage of the total reimbursement. Sounds logical, right? Well...read on!

The reality

You send out your bills to insurances. Ideally, they all should be paid quickly and correctly. However, in reality, about half will be paid more or less on time. The other half will be... "forgotten"! And this is where outsourcing fails. The bills that insurances "forget" still need to be dealt with and dealt with vigorously, otherwise you will never see your money. You need to call the insurances and find out why the bills were not paid. This is called **follow-up,** or more to the point, **"bitching"**. You need to get on the phone and find out if the bills were received and if yes, why they were not processed. If they have not been received, they need to be resent. I am yet to see an outside billing service that actually does any vigorous bitching. In fact bitching alone is not enough. Some bills will be paid incorrectly, or downcoded, or rebundled and need to be disputed. On the face of it, a billing company has every reason to bitch and dispute, since the more money they collect, the more they get paid. Remember, they get paid a percentage of reimbursement. However, bitching and disputing take a lot of time and are no fun at all. Instead of spending their time bitching, billing companies simply sign up another doctor. The time they should spend bitching for your unpaid bills is instead spend sending out the bills of this second doctor, or third, fourth. Sending out the bills takes no time at all. A single biller could probably handle 10 or more doctors, if all he does is send out the bills, collects a percentage of whatever money comes in and "forgets" the bitching. This is a very easy job. Since outsourced billers do not bitch and dispute vigorously enough, you should never outsource this important function. You should keep in house and make sure your biller follows-up on all unpaid bills and continues to do so until they are all paid.

The professional way to bitch: tricks of the trade

As I said, in my experience, only about half of your bills will be paid correctly and on time without any additional work by you. The other half needs extra effort. What exactly happens with all these "lost" or "forgotten" bills? Theories abound. Rumor has it that insurances simply throw them away, knowing that many doctors never follow-up. This, of course, saves insurances a lot of money.

When you call and ask why you have not been paid, you get to hear:

We never received the bill, as in "it got lost in the mail" or, if sent electronically, it simply did not arrive, it was lost in cyberspace. Right! If I had a dollar for every bill that was lost inexplicably I would have retired to Yuma by now! Malicious souls say insurances simply throw away a certain percentage of the bills they receive to save money. They know that many doctors don't bother to keep tabs on what bills where not paid and don't even notice the losses. I heard other, equally malicious theories. For example, each bill processor at an insurance company is required to process a certain number of bills each day. In order to clear their desks, these people simply throw away the bills left on their desks at the end of the day. All this under the approving eyes of their supervisors. The purpose is, again, saving money. Are these allegations true? Who knows! It is a fact that an inordinate number of bills get "lost". It seems unlikely that they are lost accidentally. The number is simply too large.

What to do about it: Resend the bill, write on it "second submission" (there is a field on the form where you can do that, namely box 19) and document in your billing notes whom you spoke to at the insurance. A week later call again and make sure the second submission arrived and is being processed.

The bill is in processing. This is code for "we have the bill, but we're not going to pay it".

What to do about it: Tell the insurance that their payment will be late and therefore you expect to be paid interest. Make a note of the conversation. If they pay you late and no interest is attached, call them again and request your interest.

The bill is stuck in the system, also code for "we're not gonna pay".

What to do about it: Ask what needs to be done to get it unstuck. Tell them it's their job to get it unstuck and call again a week later to see what happened. Take names and make a note. If next week it is still "stuck", ask to speak with a supervisor and definitely demand interest.

The bill is in medical review. This may be a genuine occurrence, rather than a delay tactic. It may mean it was an unusual situation and someone with more experience is looking at it. It could be a new procedure, or anything that the original processor is not familiar with.

What to do about it: Ask to speak with the person who reviews it and see what the hold-up is. Getting hold of this person will be very difficult. It is often a "medical director" of some sort, but you don't need to talk to him on the phone. You can write him a letter and fax it to him. Don't forget to mention you are looking forward to receiving interest! A week later call again and again and again until you get paid.

We need notes, for example operative reports. This request is very common whenever you are dealing with Medicaid plans.

What to do about it: Send them all the notes, not only those they request, but everything that could have even the remotest bearing on the case. Take names, make notes and call again a week later to see if they received them.

You get the picture. The kaleidoscope of excuses for not paying your bills is endless. The point is, you need to remain a pain in their side until you see the money. In some cases it takes months and tens of phone calls to get paid, but if you don't do it, you worked for free. Now you see why outsourcing does not work; nobody wants to make all these phone calls!

What is the purpose of all this bitching?

The insurances know which offices are hard-nosed and which ones are softies. You want to have a reputation of being a tough customer. That decreases the chance of future hassles. In fact, the more you bitch now, the less you'll have to bitch in the future! However, no matter how dedicated you are, some insurances are such a pain that your only option is to stop accepting their patients. More about that in future chapters.

PEARL OF WISDOM

How long should you wait until you start calling on unpaid bills? The answer is, **all bills that are more than 3 weeks old and have not been paid, need work**. Don't wait longer than that, because the longer you wait, the longer it's going to take to get paid.

Billing patients

What about patients who don't pay their bills?

When you receive a payment from an insurance you may have to bill a patient for co-insurance or deductible. Patients are just as keen to pay their bills as insurances, namely not very! I recommend the following procedure: send out your bill and write on it **"due now"**. If no payment arrives within 30 days, send out another bill and write on it that if no money is received within 14 days, the bill will be sent to a collection agency and a collection fee will be charged. Some offices call the patients on the phone, try to be nice, try to coax them to pay, etc. I advise against that. It takes a lot of time and in my experience it rarely leads anywhere. Instead, if no money is received after the 14 day warning, send the bill to a collection agency without further warning. From that point on, you don't do anything anymore with that particular bill. It is in the hands of the collection agency. That is what they get paid to do. The surcharge added by the collection agency reimburses the agency for its work. In my experience patients are divided into two categories: those who pay their bills on time and those who will wind up in collections. Calling them and trying to "remind" them leads nowhere. It is best to show that you are serious about getting paid and send them to collections. After all, patients talk to each other and if you get a reputation that one can ignore your bills, you are done for!

PEARL OF WISDOM

When patients come to see you for the first time, i.e., when you first register them, make them sign a paper that **warns them about bills left unpaid**. In my office they need to sign the following:

"...I understand that I am responsible for all charges regardless of insurance coverage. I agree to pay my account with this office in accordance with the regular rates and payment terms of this office. **If my account is referred for collection, I agree to pay reasonable collection expenses including attorney's fees.**

Checks accepted only upon the following terms: if any check is returned unpaid, the office or authorized agent may then debit my checking account for the amount of the check, a $25.00 service charge, plus any actual charges assessed by this office's financial institution as a result of the dishonored check, as provided for by A.R.S. 44-6852. Payment by check constitutes acceptance of these terms..."

You need to have the patients sign this sort of warning, otherwise they will act surprised when the collection agency starts collecting.

Another PEARL OF WISDOM

A patient that was sent to collections should be discharged from your care. This should be done in writing and I trust you know how to do that. If you don't, you need to learn. Not everybody agrees on this measure, but I think you must avoid patients who don't pay their bills. Remember, they expect you to deal with them professionally, on time and with compassion. It is their right to expect that. It is your right to expect payment!

Yet another PEARL OF WISDOM

Collect all co-payments upfront, when the patients come in. If you don't collect upfront and bill them later, you run the risk of not getting paid. Some patients moan and groan about it. The moaning is an early warning sign! It says that particular patient is not planning to pay his bills. The moaners need to be told in no uncertain terms that the co-payments are due now and that there are no exceptions. If they don't have money with them or a check book, tell them to go to the bank and get the money. But **careful: make sure they don't have an urgent medical problem and make sure you don't tell them off in front of other waiting patients!** If they have an emergency, deal with the emergency first and with the money later!

Exceptions

Every rule has an exception. I advocate that you show leniency with patients who are very poor, or who have a dreadful disease. Let's say you have just diagnosed someone with pancreas cancer and he owes you a $50 deductible. I would send out a bill, but I would leave it at that. I would not send a 14 day warning, nor would I send that particular patient to collections. That patient has much worse worries than paying your 50 bucks! Leave him alone!

How about payment plans?

Some patients think that as long as they send you a nominal amount each month, you cannot send them to collections. Nonsense! You have no legal obligation to accept "trickle-in" payments. If a patient owes you $1000 and demands you accept monthly payments of $ 50, it will take a long time to pay off his debt. You are not a bank. Tell the patient the payment is due in full and that you do not provide financing for your patients. There are many doctors who work out "payment plans". I am against them because it adds to your workload. You have to keep reminding the patient to send in his payment, keep track of what was paid, etc. That is the job of a collection agency.

Remember, patients talk to each other all the time. Why are you taught to deny requests for narcotics? Because word spreads rapidly and soon you will have an office full of drug seekers. The same applies to unpaid bills. If you get a reputation as a "forgiving" creditor, you'll have many more slow paying patients. However, your own bills keep coming in: the rent, the malpractice insurance, taxes. Try to be late in paying your personnel and see what happens! Since nobody forgives you your bills, why should you forgive your patients' bills?

To accept or not accept credit cards

This is a judgment call. I do not. The machine for processing credit cards is expensive, last time I looked about $ 1,000! In addition, the credit card companies charge you a percentage of the amount processed. Last time I looked it was 3%. This means you have to increase your billed amount by that percentage to collect what is rightfully yours. Not accepting credit cards has not been a problem for our office. Whenever you have a patient who insists he has a credit card and nothing else, tell him to go to the bank and get cash advance on his card and pay you cash.

Billing software

You have no choice but to buy a product from a small vendor. Unlike software for writing notes, where you can buy something off-the-shelf (like Word) there is no off-the-shelf billing software! I strongly caution you to watch the price. Many packages cost thousands and thousands of dollars. The software may be ok, but spending $10,000 on software is simply too much money, in my judgment. Also, some of these software packages require you to buy a separate hardware system. For example an expensive computer workstation, that does not run on Windows and therefore does not run anything else but the billing software. Don't do that.

If you want to get a picture of what software is available, the best place where you can see them all in one room is the Annual Meeting of the American Society of Whateveryourspecialtyis. You can spend a day talking with the vendors and see what tickles your fancy. However, if you are a beginner, you have no fancy to tickle yet, since you don't know what features are relevant and what is fluff.

If you want my advice, buy something cheap, something less than $ 1,500. That way, if the software is junk, you did not lose too much money.

I use a program called **Lytec,** which costs about $ 1,200. You can buy it from a vendor called MedTek Solutions, or www.medtek-solutions.com. If they don't have a branch in your area, ask them to refer you to a local vendor. No, they don't pay me kickbacks for recommending them.

Lytec is comparatively cheap and the vendor provides good support. Another important feature about Lytec is that it does billings, scheduling and nothing else. Unlike other packages, which try to solve all your software needs. Would I buy Lytec again, if I were to do it all over gain? Yes, because I have not seen anything cheaper. However, I have not been to the Annual Meeting of the Fleas in a long time!

PEARL OF WISDOM

Never buy software that requires you to buy a specialized computer system to run it. Whatever you buy, make sure it runs on Windows!

Practical billing

Billing cannot be taught in a book. You need to sit down with your software and learn how to enter the required information, what buttons to push to send bills out electronically, on paper, how to write off amounts, how to account for partial payments, etc. It is a big job, but you must learn it. I repeat **YOU, THE DOCTOR MUST BE THE EXPERT BILLER IN YOUR OFFICE.** You are not going to do the actual punching of the buttons. You have a hired biller for that. But you must know how to supervise the biller and for that you must have in-depth knowledge of the process itself.

Clearinghouses

The modern way to send out bills is electronically, not via mail. The software fills out the infamous HCFA-1500 form and sends it out as bits and bytes over the phone line. Theoretically, you can send the bills directly to an insurance. For example, via the insurance web site. I do not recommend this method, because the kinks have not been worked out yet and HIPAA has made things more complicated for the time being. However, this is the wave of the future. Since the future is not here yet, read on.

- **Send the bills to a clearinghouse, which will send them to insurances.** They can do it electronically, or they can drop them to paper and mail them. There will be a charge for using a clearing house. I pay $50 a month. It is money well spent, because electronic bills are processed and paid much faster by insurances than paper bills. The software you use to create the bills dictates what clearinghouse you can use, because one program may not work with all clearinghouses. The software vendor will tell you which clearinghouse to use.

THE MOTHER OF ALL PEARLS OF WISDOM

I've told you this before, but it merits repeating here: **YOU MUST DO THE CODING YOURSELF. YOU, <u>NOT THE BILLER!</u>** Before you can send out bills, you need to code your patient encounters. Coding cannot be learned on the fly. Take your time and learn it well. Coding translates directly into dollars. Did you hear me? DIRECTLY! In fact you should code all your encounters as soon as you finish with the patient. After coding, you give the code to your biller, who will send it out. **Don't let the biller code based on your notes. Billers are NOTORIOUS undercoders** and undercoding will cost you tens of thousands of dollars!

If you don't know anything about coding you need to learn it and learn it well before you even think of private practice. The best way to learn is by taking a coding/billing course at a local community college. This can be done in the evening. It will take many months, but you would be foolish to go into business and not know how to code.

How soon to send out the bills?

The faster, the better. There are doctors who send out their bills only once a week, for example when their dictations come in. But you are smarter than that. You don't dictate, you have computerized records. Therefore, **you send out the bills every day.** Here is how to do it:

- **You see the patient.**
- **You write your note,** either on your PDA, or you go back to your office and sit down at the main computer.
- **You fill out the ICD and CPT codes on your "superbill".**
- **At the end of the day, you drop all your superbills on the desk of your biller.**
- **The next morning, the biller sends out the bills for the previous day.** I advise you to do today's billings the next day simply because you might get called during the night and may have additional bills to add to the batch.

What on earth is a "superbill"?

It is simply a sheet of paper on which you list the procedures you do most frequently, the patient's name, insurance and date of service. This allows you to code quickly. I never understood why it is called "superbill", since there is nothing "super" about it, but the name is well established. It makes it sound like it is something awesome, complicated and hard to deal with. It is in fact simplicity itself and a very useful tool to have.

Books for billers

Every year, you must order the new Medicare reimbursement, CPT and ICD books:

Current Procedural Terminology, which is a book of codes that assigns a 5 digit number to everything you can possibly do to a patient, from an office visit to a brain transplant. Published by the American Medical Association, costs ~$60, order at 800/621-8335

International Classification of Diseases, a book that assigns a number to every disease known to mankind. I get mine from Practice Management Information Corporation (PMIC) for ~$55. Contact www.pmiconline.com or 800/med-shop, or 4727 Wilshire Blvd #300 Los Angeles, CA 90010

Medicare Part B Arizona Provider Disclosure Report, which has all Medicare reimbursement information for Arizona. Costs ~$10. Call 877/908-8431, or contact Medicare Service Center 4305 13th Avenue Fargo, ND 58103-3373

How do you know if your billings are done right?

Imagine yourself up and running. The patients are coming in large numbers, your staff is competent and pleasant, you are sending out bills and you are bitching to beat the band! There is actually money coming in, but how do you know if you are getting paid correctly and promptly? Here is how you do it: **you watch the "accounts receivable"!** Ah, what on earth is that? Now you are entering that forbidding land nobody wants to visit: accounting! You are seeing visions of pinstriped suits whispering in marble halls, making shady deals and establishing secret handshakes, tweaking the balance sheet Enron-style, filling their pockets with gold. Too bad these were not your pockets!

The yardstick by which to measure your billings: the accounts receivable

In accountant's English, each patient is an "account". The sum of all patients is called the "receivables", i.e., all bills you sent out and are waiting on payment. Incidentally, there are also "accounts payable", which is the sum of all bills sent to you by your vendors, such as rent, insurance and office supplies.

Your billings software will give you a report of the accounts receivable. It is a long list of all patients whose bills have not been paid yet. The payments are broken down by the following categories:

- **Current:** these are bills that are less then 30 days old
- **30 – 60 days:** these are bills that are less then 60 days old
- **60 – 90 days:** these are bills that are less then 90 days old
- **> 90 days:** these are bills that are more than 90 days old

For each category the software will give you the amount outstanding and the percentage of your charges. These numbers will be listed at the end of the report, which can be many pages long. In fact you want it to be many pages long, because it would mean you saw lots of patients! To explain how you interpret these numbers, let's look at the accounts receivable distribution for the practice I manage. At this point in time, the distribution is:

- **Current:** ~ 71%
- **30 – 60 days:** ~ 15%
- **60 – 90 days:** ~ 4%
- **> 90 days:** ~ 9 %

This distribution is close to ideal. What is good about it? Most of the bills are "young", or recent, i.e., <2 months old. The categories "current" and "30-60 days" include the newest bills and also bills for which we have already started to bitch! Remember, all bills that are more then 3 weeks old and have not been paid are placed in the "bitching folder". All these bills are called every week to see why the insurances have not paid.

Categories "60-90 days" and ">90 days" include bills sent to secondary insurances, which are always delayed. You have to wait for the EOB from the primary insurance before you can bill the secondary insurance. They also include bills for which the bitching has not been effective. At least not yet. These are bills that are disputed and where the bitching is particularly vicious and protracted. They also contain bills from insurances that are very slow to pay, no matter how much we bitch! These are contracts I will likely cancel soon. More about this in future chapters.

Notice I said the distribution is "close" to ideal, but not "ideal". Ideally, the amount in the category ">90 days" should be <5%, in my opinion. This is money that will either come in very late, or not come in at all. All bills older than 60 days need to be worked vigorously. When we're dealing with insurances that are this slow to pay, we bitch loudly. The gloves really come off! We're talking nastigrams to supervisors, letters to the insurance commissioner, the works!

If the distribution above is "close to ideal", what would be a distribution "far from ideal"? It would look like this:
- **Current:** ~ 5 %
- **30 – 60 days:** ~ 10 %
- **60 – 90 days:** ~ 20 %
- **> 90 days:** ~ 65 %

Notice this distribution is skewed towards the delayed categories. **This practice is in very serious trouble!** Many bills currently in the category "> 60 days" were likely ignored by the insurances. They were "lost" for some reason or another. If you were to resubmit these bills, many insurances will tell you that it is too late, i.e., that you passed the deadline for submission! When that happens, you can kiss that money good-bye! That is precisely why we start our bitching at three weeks! To avoid missing the deadline for submission. That is also the reason why we mark the resubmitted bills "second submission" in the appropriate box in form HCFA-1500 and why we take names and make notes of all telephone conversations with insurances. That way, if it ever gets close to the deadline, we can document the delay is due to insurance error not ours.

PEARL OF WISDOM

Never allow your accounts receivable to be skewed like in the example noted above. Money at >60 days is money you will likely have to write off! There is no better yardstick by which to measure your biller's performance than the distribution of the accounts receivable. **This report must be printed and examined closely every month without fail!**

How to receive your payments?

Ideally, you should ask insurances to deposit the dough directly into your practice checking account. Medicare does this and a handful of other commercial plans too. All others send checks. **Do not have the checks mailed to the office.** Sometimes staff cannot resist the temptation of grabbing some of your money. It's human nature, what can I say! However, money that does not come to the office cannot be stolen by anybody in the office. **Have your checks mailed to a post office box, or to your house.** Personally, I favor the latter solution, because I'm too cheap to pay for a box!

How do you know if you got paid correctly?

Most doctors I know don't even glance at the EOBs. This is a cardinal mistake! The only way to know if you got paid correctly is by examining the EOB closely. Examining the EOBs will tell you:

- **Did insurance pay for the same code you billed, or was your bill downcoded/rebundled?** If so, you need to dispute it.
- **If the insurance coded it correctly, were you paid correctly?** Compare the amount received with the fee schedule in the contract. Don't skip this step simply because it involves opening a drawer and pulling out a sheet of paper and comparing numbers. You can make a cheat-sheet, if it will make this easier.
- **The practice of examining the EOB will have a very important side-effect:** over time, you will get a feel for how much money you make from the things you do in the office. This will allow you to tailor the services to maximize income. For example, if you remove 2 moles on the same day, you only get paid 50% for the second one. Best to bring the patient back and get paid 100%!

Incidentally, **you, the doctor must read your EOBs first. Don't "trust" your biller to uncover all the tricks insurances play on you** (see below).

Tricks of the trade: things insurances will do to maximize their income

Let's be realistic: income maximization is not a sport you invented. Insurances do that too. Favorite tools include:

- **Downcoding.** A common occurrence. When you see this on the EOB you must bitch with great intensity. Otherwise insurances will make a habit of it.
- **Bundling.** Let's say you did 2 procedures, a sigmoidoscopy and you burned off some actinic keratosis. The insurance sends you an EOB where the burning is "forgotten" and a note saying your bill was rebundled based on "insurance guidelines" (which guidelines can be changed by the insurance any time it pleases). The burning of the AKs was found to be "incidental" to the sigmoidoscopy and therefore not separately reimbursable. You would think that looking up someone's ass and treating a skin lesion would be considered two separate procedures by any thinking human being. Welcome to insurance logic. Remember, their purpose is to save money. They hope you will miss it and not complain. However, you are a smart businessman and of course you catch it. Then you bitch!
- **Forgetting to add interest.** If payment comes later than noted in the contract, insurances need to pay interest. How often do they "forget"? Often! Bitch!
- **Denying e/m encounters billed with modifiers 25 and 57.** Insurance logic turns particularly pernicious here. Their argument is that an e/m evaluation is "incidental" to the surgery performed subsequently. Bull! It is a separate encounter and it needs to be paid. Period. If an insurance systematically refuses to pay, consider sending two separate bills. First the one for the surgery. Wait for it to be paid, and then send the one for the e/m encounter. Maybe they will not notice the two bills cover the same date. If they do, consider bringing the patient back on a different day to do the surgery. If an insurance consistently refuses to pay for these two modifiers, strongly consider canceling the contract. Remember, you don't ever want to work for free!

Finally, don't hesitate to dispute all bills that were paid incorrectly. It is a mistake to let such things go. You worked hard for the money. Patients expect you to treat them well and rightfully so. You should insist on correct and timely payment. Remember that your rent, staff salaries, insurance, office supplies cannot be "downcoded". Try paying your secretary late or less than agreed and see what happens. Why should you accept shoddy treatment from insurance? Occasionally, no matter how much you bitch, some insurances simply do not pay. Your only recourse then is to stop seeing their patients. This will be addressed later in the chapter on business strategies.

Chapter 7:
MALPRACTICE INSURANCE AND DEFENSIVE MEDICINE

Motto: Said the patient to the doctor, "Doc, I can break your finger. I can also break all ten!"

We spend our entire careers under the threat of malpractice suits. For many of us the threat becomes reality. Any text on practice management would be incomplete without a discussion of this subject.

Doctors believe the current malpractice misery was brought upon the medical community by some evil entity, such as trial lawyers and greedy patients. The truth is that we doctors ourselves are responsible! Surprised to hear this? Read on!

Why do American doctors get sued?

The complete question should be "Why do American doctors get sued, and doctors in other countries don't?" The option to sue a doctor in this country rests on two pillars:

- **The willingness of other doctors to testify against their colleagues.** Malpractice suits are usually judged in front of a jury. However, they are highly technical cases and lay juries cannot be expected to understand them. The "explaining" is done by expert witnesses, namely the aforementioned doctors, who testify against their own kind! For money, of course. Always for money.
- **Contingency fees.** Under US law, a plaintiff can file a suit at no cost. The suit is financed by the plaintiff's lawyer. The lawyer gets paid only if the suit is successful, in which case he receives a portion of the jury award. If there is a settlement, the lawyer is paid out of the settlement amount. If there is no award, the lawyer pays the costs of the lawsuit and the plaintiff is charged nothing at all. Not so in other countries. Contingency fees are forbidden and a plaintiff would have to finance the entire lawsuit, not knowing if he is going to win. If he loses, he pays all the trial costs: not only his own, but also the winning party's, the court fees and sometimes a fine for having put the defendant through a trial. One of the most pernicious consequences of the US system is that it "forces" lawyers to litigate a lot. Since they are paid only if they win, they have no choice but to file numerous lawsuits, hoping

that some of them will result in payment. This money must cover all expenses, namely those generated by successful as well as failed suits. Therefore, lawyers are quite "trigger happy". This eagerness to file suits has extended to the general population. The prevailing attitude is "Let's go to court, maybe we'll get lucky and come back home millionaires. If we don't succeed, it does not cost anything". The tort laws were the first American national lottery.

However, the problem is not so much the laws. In my view, the **problem is the willingness of doctors to sit in judgment of their colleagues**. For money, of course.

PEARL OF WISDOM

All malpractice litigation is about money. Don't you ever believe it is about "justice", "adequate compensation", "closure" or any such nonsense. It is always about money. Remember this: **wherever there is a guy with money, there is an army of other guys who want to take it away from him.** As a group, doctors are perceived to be rich and therefore natural magnets for tort litigation. The same applies to any other group with "deep pockets"! If a house burns down, do you think the fireman who held the hose will be sued? No, the suit will be against the city who hired the fireman. The city has the deeper pockets!

The expert witness dissected

A lawyer who files a malpractice suit must find an expert witness to testify on behalf of the patient and against the accused doctor. **No expert witness, no case!** Unfortunately, there is no shortage of willing candidates.

What sort of doctors are these? I don't profess to know what is going on in their heads, but from personal observation I can draw at least some partial conclusions:

- **Doctors with an ax to grind**, for example docs who were mistreated during residency and who think this is a way to get back at the "establishment".
- **Self-righteous doctors,** who think they are so good and so unlikely to make mistakes, they feel perfectly entitled to point fingers at their peers. This is a variant of "playing God". For money, mind you!
- **Greedy doctors,** who stumbled upon this opportunity to make money. More on this later.

- **Doctors who truly think they provide a valuable service to society.** What can I say?!
- **Old guys who can't quite retire.** Too old to swing a scalpel, but not old enough to call it quits. The expert witnessing provides them with an opportunity to make an easy buck, without the hassles of being in practice.

The case of the expert witness, or when in doubt, rationalize!

Doctors who engage in this kind of "work" rarely brag about it. They keep it very "hush-hush", very much undercover. I am convinced that deep down all these doctors know they are engaging in a highly questionable behavior. Yet there is no shortage of attempts to rationalize it.

- **If I don't do it, somebody else will.** I don't think so. I am convinced that if more and more doctors said "NO" to these requests, we would all benefit.
- **I provide a valuable service.** So do prostitutes!
- **I love the money.** Every now and then you run into an honest chap. However, <u>the money you cash in with the right hand by being an expert witness is immediately spent with the left hand in form of high malpractice insurance premiums</u>. After all, the expert witness needs to buy insurance too.
- **It is a matter of principle, if someone is injured, he should be compensated.** Ah, what a great argument! If that is so, why do you insist on getting paid? If you are so principled, do it for free! Yet I have never seen an expert witness waive his fees. The fees are very high. Hourly rates of $ 400 or more are commonplace. It is easy money, because all you do is render an opinion. You incur no personal risk and suffer no career set-back either.
- **The medical profession has some bad apples. I help keep the number of bad apples low.** This is perhaps the most malicious argument of them all. The underlying tenor is that the expert witness is somehow a "better" doctor than the one being sued and therefore morally entitled judge him. Is the expert witness so sure he will never make a mistake? Never come to the wrong conclusion? Always have 20/20 vision, not just in hindsight? These self appointed moral apostles are just as likely to make mistakes as the next guy. If the apostle makes a mistake and kills a patient, is he going to offer compensation to the family? Bull! He is going to paper it over, just like anybody else! The second underlying assumption is that the threat of being sued will make a careless doctor careful. This is utter nonsense. A dumb doctor will always be dumb, no matter how many lawsuits he loses.

PEARL OF WISDOM

Whenever you hear somebody say "it's not the money", you can be absolutely certain IT IS THE MONEY!

What to do with injured patients?

The issue of what to do with patients who were injured by doctors is a societal one. Medical malpractice is a small slice of a very big pie. It is completely unreasonable to ask an individual profession to solve this problem. The issue was far more complex, because it involves all tort legislation. What should be done for anybody, not just patients, who are injured? What is negligence? A doctor failing to diagnose a difficult case, or a doctor who shows up in the OR drunk? Should compensation ever be paid for complaints that are not measurable, such as pain and suffering? How do you know if I have pain or I am just faking it, hoping to go home with a million bucks? I understand paying a guy some money if he lost a leg, but how about people who mourn the loss of a pet? Speaking for myself, I could mourn quite convincingly for a million bucks. I imagine in this respect I am not alone! As discussed above, the expert witness does not keep the money earned from this "work". He is a participant in a circle of money; he touches it, but does not hold on to it. He needs to pay his expenses too (such as malpractice insurance) and therefore his "gain" is in fact no gain at all. Monetarily, being an expert witness is a +/- zero sum activity!

The ice-cold, undeniable reality.

- **The threat of a lawsuit never turned a dumb doctor into a smart one, a careless one into a careful one or an incompetent one into a competent one, BUT HAS TURNED ALL DOCTORS INTO EXPENSIVE ONES!** After all, the costs of malpractice insurance are passed on to patients directly and immediately. This makes medicine overall much more expensive than it would be without lawsuits. Remember, costly malpractice insurance is not the only expense generated by this threat. We doctors are forced to practice defensive medicine; we do a lot of things that are not in the patient's interest, but are aimed solely at decreasing the risk of a suit.
- **The threat of lawsuits has killed the doctor-patient relationship in this country.** Trust me on this one: the traditional doctor-patient relationship, as it was meant to be, does not exist in the US. All patients are regarded as potential headaches and dealt with as such, namely in a cold and bureaucratic manner. In fact, most

doctors are not even aware of the chill between themselves and their patients, because this is the only atmosphere they have ever known. To understand what I am talking about, picture yourself dealing with a patient who cannot possibly sue you. It goes without saying that you would be much more relaxed than you currently are. Being free of fear of litigation would allow you to concentrate on the medical matters and forget about the myriad things we do to cover our asses. Things that are neither medically needed, nor in the patient's interest. You would look at the patient as a human being in need and not as a potential enemy in a lawsuit. It would make a major difference. It would allow you to establish a doctor-patient relationship!

- **Because of the litigation threat we cannot trust our patients.** That is precisely why friendships with patients are discouraged. You heard the saying "treat them and street them". The public at large is engaged in a permanent debate on how to find a doctor you can trust. However, for doctors that is not the issue at all. The issue is that we, the doctors cannot trust our patients! In other parts of the world the mutual trust between doctors and patients is a sacred bond. The matters discussed with the doctor are entirely confidential; they are not meant for public consumption, such as in a court of law. It is thought to be self-evident that the doctor would not break this relationship based on mutual trust. At the same time, it is thought to be just as self evident that the patient would not break it either. Patients who run to court looking to get rich break this trust in a most egregious way. The consequence is the loss of the traditional doctor-patient relationship and the birth of cover-your-ass medicine. Both doctors and patients are losers in this game, but I think the patients are the bigger losers. After all they foot the bill for their own greed.

- **Cover your ass** is a way of life for all doctors, as indeed it must be. Defensive medicine is prohibitively expensive, but simply unavoidable in a world where you cannot trust your clients!

- **You will be sued!** It is not a matter of "if", but "when". Adjust your mental attitude beforehand, that way you don't need to be "devastated" when it happens. Buy good insurance, protect your assets and understand the principles of defensive medicine (see below).

- **Practicing "good medicine" will not protect you.** Frivolous suits occur every day. Not only that, but you can lose a trial for having made the wrong judgment call!

And last be not least:

STOP BLAMING THE LAWYERS FOR THE MALPRACTICE MESS WE ARE IN. THIS IS A PROBLEM WE DOCTORS HAVE BROUGHT UPON OURSELVES. REMEMBER, NO EXPERT WITNESS, NO CASE. STOP TESTIFYING AGAINST YOUR COLLEAGUES AND THE PROBLEM GOES AWAY.

The lawyers are merely taking advantage of a business opportunity presented to them by the doctors!

The malpractice mess, day one

To the extent there ever was a day one, I picture it like this: the doctor, the lawyer and the insurance agent sat together at a table in the golf club dining room. Says the doctor to the lawyer:

"Sue me! That way I can start performing all sorts of unnecessary medicine, tests and procedures, which I will, of course, bill to the patients. Admittedly, I will incur some costs from being sued, but I expect I will make up the loss by doing all these unnecessary things and billing them to my patients, who will have no choice, but to pay them. Incidentally, since you are going to need an expert witness, my cousin, who is sitting at the next table, already agreed to help you."

The lawyer answered:

"What a great idea! I wish I had thought of it first. After all, the laws allow me to file frivolous suit after frivolous suit. Eventually, I will win a suit and we all go out and celebrate!"

The insurance agent piped-in:

"What a great idea! Why didn't I think of it? I can start selling malpractice insurance. It will be expensive and all you docs will have to buy it. You will pass the costs on to the patients. There will be all this money going around and ultimately the patient picks up the final tab!"

The discussion is overheard by the owner of a medical lab, a manufacturer of medical equipment, a manufacturer of office equipment, the owner of a risk management consulting company and the owner of a courier service. They all came over and joined in the discussion. They envisioned a world where all of them would profit, if only the lawyer would start suing! And he did. The rest is history.

The point is nowadays many businesses profit from malpractice suits; I think it is unrealistic to expect improvement. After all, nobody wants to give up on an opportunity to make a buck. It is important to realize that suing for malpractice is a very big enterprise, involving not only doctors and lawyers, but a host of other businesses. Just think of all the CT scanners manufactured simply to fill the need generated by defensive medicine! Paradoxically, doctors themselves profit from the threat of malpractice suits. Just think of how many referrals to specialists a GP generates just to cover his ass. Referrals that are neither medically necessary nor in the patient's interest. Referrals that feed a lot of specialists who otherwise would not even exist. All this "extra medicine" is, of course, charged to the patients. I wish patients could understand this: the more they sue, the more it costs them. Certainly, those who win suits profit handsomely; but overall the patient population in this country pays dearly for its own greed.

The solution

I think the time has come to look the problem in the eye and act upon it. **No expert witness, no case.** One could make a valid argument that we, the doctors, all of us, need to apply pressure on those who testify against us and try to stop them. So far, this "work" had no consequences for the perpetrators. What if it did?

- **When a specialist solicits your business ask him if he ever testified against his colleagues**. If he did, tell him you will not refer patients to him. After all, how do you know he will not testify against you too?
- **When you look to add a partner to your group don't hire a doctor with this sort of past.** The reason is the same: you don't know when he'll turn against you.
- **When you hear doctors talking about their work as expert witnesses tell them what you thing of those who testify against their colleagues.** Tell them you would not do business with them. Point them out in public. Tell them in no uncertain terms what you think of them.
- **Instead of testifying against your colleagues, TESTIFY FOR THEM!** There is money to be made that way too. Doctors who get sued need an expert witness too. More about it in the chapter on diversification.

In the recent past, I read about doctors who attacked lawyers for filing frivolous suits. The doctors sued the lawyers hoping to put the fear of God into them. Lawyers, of course, make a tempting target. However, going after the lawyers is barking up the wrong tree. The lawyers have no choice but to file frivolous suits! They only get paid if they win. Since they don't win all cases, they must file lots of them to increase the odds of winning.

After all, only those who play the lottery can win. Doctors who sue lawyers are wasting their time. They fail to identify the true culprit, which is the expert witness.

The standard of care

The standard of care is defined as whatever a prudent doctor would have done faced with the same situation. However, **it is a fantasy concept**. It is a creation of the courts, i.e., of lay people. It seems quite logical on the face of it. However, the underlying assumption is that there is a "right" and a "wrong" way to deal with every medical situation. Not so! Practicing medicine means weighing options and making judgment calls. Few things are black and white. As far as I know, the concept of standard of care does not exist in other countries. The "standard" is whatever a doctor did in a particular situation. It is thought to be self-evident that you cannot second-guess an expert who has applied his knowledge and common sense to a particular problem. In most countries doctors are **not** held to a standard of care, instead they enjoy **"freedom of treatment"**. At first glance this seems illogical. How can you allow a doctor to do whatever he wants? However, if everybody applies the same "standard", how can anybody become an outstanding expert? After all, there are "famous" doctors and less famous ones. The famous ones became renowned precisely because they applied innovative methods in a continuous effort to improve their treatments. They stray from the "standard" in search of better ways. Now you begin to see what a bunch of non-sense this "standard of care" really is. **How do you introduce new treatments, new drugs and new tests in a world where doctors are bound to follow the "standard of care"?** Any new lab test, any new surgical procedure is a breach with this standard. Does this mean we stop being innovative? No, of course not! You see therefore, in everyday practice the "standard" is breached all the time. Why is it such an iron clad requirement in malpractice cases? Incidentally, Penicillin was against the standard of care when it was introduced!

An example: Two days ago, my 6 year-old son came home from school with a sore throat and a fever. A rapid strep test was negative. Today he is well, the soreness is gone and his temperature is normal. The tonsils looked normal when he got sick and still look normal now. He is back in school and running around. Great, you'll say. Well, not quite. Today, i.e., 48 hours after he got sick and about 12 hours after he became well again the lab calls and tells me the culture is positive for group A strep. You are the doctor, you decide what should be done with a child who was sick for 2 days and now is well, but has a positive strep culture. What is the standard of care? It is a given that if I ask any doctor in America what to do, he will say to treat with Penicillin, even though the kid is well. This is "cover your ass medicine" in its chemically purest form! But is it the right thing to do for the kid? Do I treat the lab result or the patient? You decide! And don't forget to write a note explaining what you did and hope it will save you when I sue you! If you say not to treat I will sue you and argue you put my kid at risk for rheumatic fever. If you say to give Penicillin I will sue you for unnecessary use of antibiotics. Needless to say, the literature on this particular subject is unclear. You can easily find an expert witness for either case. Yet this is "bread-and-butter medicine". If this does not allow an easy decision, defensible under the "standard of care" principle, what about truly complicated things? When is a renal transplant rejected? According to whose criteria? When does a tumor become inoperable? When is it too late/too early to induce a delivery? Who has the final decision on this stuff? The clinician in charge of the patient or the "expert" witness later on?

The public expects perfection

Nowadays the public expects the doctors to be perfect. Needless to say, it is a completely unrealistic expectation. Yet it is fueled by our behavior. When a patient gets in your face and gives you a third degree you should not just sit there and take it. The correct answer is, "My dear patient, I am a human being just like you. Sometimes I get it right, sometimes I don't. You have to live with that. If you can't, you need to find another doctor". The patients have every right to expect you to take them seriously, be available, educate yourself and keep up-to-date, be nice and use your best judgment. That is what they pay for. But patients have no right to view doctors as sources for million-dollar awards every time the best judgment was not good enough!

Practical defensive medicine

Since your notes are so important in case of a suit, what's keeping you from writing perfect notes? Yet bad notes are written all the time. I heard that missed myocardial infarctions are a classic cause for lawsuits. Patients with chest pain are very common. Let's say you see a patient with nonspecific chest pain that does not fit any particular diagnosis. Let's further say that after thorough consideration you decide the patient does not have an MI. Well, write a non-MI note! Remember, nobody sat in the room with you. **You can write whatever you think will serve you best in case of a lawsuit!** In my opinion it is a mistake to try and document what actually happened. Instead, write what I call a "defensible note". To explain what that is, let's first write an indefensible one and then correct it.

The indefensible note

45 y/o m c/o 3 wk h/o sharp stabbing retrosternal chest pain that comes on about 15 minutes into his daily 3 mile jog. Had it 4 times so far i.e., not every time he jogs. He runs every day and only had symptoms 4 times in the past 3 wks. Lasts 5 minutes then goes away completely, radiates to the LUQ. He is short of breath, but cannot say if it is in excess of the shortness of breath caused by the running. After the pain subsides, able to continue his job w/o any problems. No other sx.

Cardiac risks: male over 45, none other

PE: normal

EKG: 1 PVC, otherwise unremarkable

A/p:

1. New onset chest pain with exercise in a patient with only 1 cardiac risk factor. Diagnosis unclear. Recommend 1 ASA qd and observation. If pain becomes more frequent or if it lasts longer, make f/u appointment and will consider exercise treadmill. Otherwise, f/u prn

What is indefensible about this note? It is wishy-washy! If you made up your mind the pain is not cardiac in origin, write a non-cardiac-pain-note! The note written above would probably come back to hunt you if he has an MI. However, the following note will serve you much better:

The defensible note

45 y/o m with several day h/o sharp, stabbing pain in L side of chest, at the costosternal junction, markedly worse with pressing on that area and with respirations, for example when breathing hard from jogging. No malaise, myalgias, cough, fever, chills, sputum, sore throat, SOB, or any other sx. No trauma. Pain comes and goes in episodes lasting a few minutes at a time, has it daily.

O: NAD, A&O
-RRR S1 + S2 +0; No JVD, edema
-LCTA
-chest wall: tender with pressure on the sore area, this reproduces the symptoms exactly
-legs: unremarkable

a/p:

1. Costochondritis: explained nature of this condition. Can be very sore, but is not serious. Patient reassured.

-rest, observe for any additional sx, such as fever, chills, cough, sputum and call if present (or come in), otherwise f/u prn
-Tylenol #3 1-2 po q 4-6 hours prn # 50; no refills

What is defensible about this note? It says "benign diagnosis of costochondritis" all over it! If the patient has an MI later and moans about you missing it, you can say the evaluation pointed to costochondritis and nowhere else. I can tell you a defense lawyer would rather defend the second note than the first!

PEARL OF WISDOM

Notes are <u>not</u> written top to bottom, but bottom to top. In English this means you first arrive at a diagnosis and then write a note that supports the diagnosis. Remember, you write notes to help you in case you get sued. Therefore help yourself and write defensible notes! Remember, we doctors are targets. We run around with big target signs painted on our foreheads. Don't ignore this, be proactive and **defend yourself**. Your first line of defense is a good note. Therefore write good notes!

Again, this assumes you made up your mind on the diagnosis. If you think the patient has cardiac chest pain, act upon it! I do not mean to teach you to blow-off your patients. But once you decided the patient does not have anything serious, don't write a note that shows you to be in doubt. Don't write notes that can be held against you. One more time, lest you misunderstand me: **TAKE YOUR PATIENTS SERIOUSLY AND GIVE THEM YOUR BEST. BUT DO NOT FORGET YOURSELF IN THE PROCESS. DON'T SERVE THE PATIENT AND SHOOT YOURSELF IN THE FOOT. COVER BOTH NEEDS, THE PATIENT'S AND YOURS!** Got it?

Types of malpractice insurance

There are two:

- **Occurrence type.** This insurance covers you for what you did during the time the insurance was in effect. Let's say you were in practice from 2003 – 2033. It is now 2035 and you are retired but you get sued for something you did in 2030. No problem! Since your insurance was in effect during the time you saw the patient, you are covered. This is "honest" insurance and very straightforward to understand. However it is very expensive! It starts at a "mature rate", unlike "claims made" policies, which start cheap and become more expensive each year, until they reach a "mature rate" after about 5 years.

- **Claims made.** With this type of insurance, two dates are important. The date you dealt with the patient and the date the suit was filed. If you retired in 2033, i.e. stopped carrying insurance after 2033 and you get sued, you are on your own! Why? Because **this type of coverage stops the day you stop paying premiums**. Even if you saw the patient during a time when the coverage was in effect, once you stop paying premiums, you are no longer covered. To extend the coverage period indefinitely, you need to buy **"tail"**. Buying "tail" turns this type of insurance into "occurrence" type insurance. Claims made insurance is cheaper than occurrence, at least initially. It starts at a low annual premium and it goes up every year until the rate "matures". The maturation process is usually five years. The logic behind this maturation process is that the longer you practice, the more likely you are to be sued. Therefore, the premium increases in proportion to the likelihood of being sued. After maturity, you may want to turn this into an "occurrence" insurance to avoid the need to buy tail in the future. However, it may be cheaper to by tail than to buy occurrence type insurance. You need to ask your broker to run the numbers.
- **Tails and noses.** A "nose" is a "reverse tail", i.e., it is insurance that covers you for the time <u>before</u> you start paying premiums. It is also called "coverage for prior acts", but referred to as "nose" in everyday talk. **Tails and noses are very important!** Make sure you understand them and know to ask about them when you buy insurance.

Let's see how it works. Let's say you are now a resident who just finished his residency and enters private practice. During your residency you are covered by a malpractice policy purchased by you residency program. The question is what happens after you finish. If the residency bought "tail", you are still covered even after you finished the program. If the residency did not buy "tail", you need to buy "nose" on your next policy in order to make sure you are covered for things you did during the residency i.e., be covered for "prior acts". This applies every time you change insurance during your professional career. **You either buy "tail" from the old carrier, or "nose" from the new carrier.** I have never heard of a residency that did not buy "tail" insurance for its residents. But it is well worth asking to make sure. Alternatively, the residency program could buy "occurrence" type insurance, where "tails" and "noses" are not an issue.

Insurance with tail, insurance with nose or occurrence-type insurance?

Which should you buy? As in many cases in the business world, the money decides! Buying tail from your old insurance may be more expensive than buying nose from the new one. Or vice-versa. At the end of your career, you will either have to buy tail from your last insurer or buy an occurrence-type policy during you last year in practice, with a nose that extends all the way to the beginning of your career, if needed.

PEARL OF WISDOM

Tails, noses and the choosing of the right type of insurance are confusing issues for the beginner. You will need a good insurance agent to hold your hand. Ask your colleagues if they can recommend a good agent.

The untold ugly truth about malpractice insurance

In my opinion, this is a classic case of insurance that's there for you **as long as you don't need it!** When you are sued, several things are likely to happen:

- **Your premium goes up.** In fact, it may go up so much as to drive you out of business. Yes, you read right! The insurance premium may become large enough to wipe out all profits from your practice! Should this happen, it would limit your career choices. That is why you may want to remain friends with the director of the local VA Hospital. Just in case you need to go beg for a job.
- **The insurance will do what is cheapest for it, not what is good for you!** In English, this means they will pressure you to settle, if they think it is cheaper for them to settle, than to defend. However, in my opinion, **a settlement is something to avoid**. A settlement hangs around your neck like a millstone, especially if it was a large one. You have to disclose it on any application you make, for any job or any insurance contract. In my judgment, it is better to go to court. If you win, it will look better on your resume than a settlement. If you lose, it will not look much worse than the settlement. Again, this is strictly my opinion. You have to decide for yourself.
- **The policy may be canceled any time the insurance thinks you smell bad**. Let's say you want to start doing a cosmetic procedure in your office, for example hair implants. From the point of view of the insurance you are now at higher risk to be sued. Not only that, but you are at considerably higher risk of frivolous suits. Cosmetic clients are more fickle than "real" patients. Also, deciding what the "standard of care" may be for a hair implant is, well,

hairy! Is it a hairline that reaches all the way down to your eyebrows or what? Consequently, rather than simply increasing your premium, the insurance may very well decide to wave "bye-bye" to you.

- **You may be considered uninsurable**. Whenever you apply for malpractice insurance, you must pass a "sniff test" to see if you may be too high a risk to insure. In insurance lingo this is called "you must pass underwriting". If you settled a case in the past, the new insurance may not want you. There is little influence you have on the outcome of the "sniff test". If the insurance doesn't want you, it will deny coverage.

PEARL OF WISDOM

A malpractice insurance policy is a document you must read with your feet in cold water. My advice is to have it reviewed by a reputable lawyer with experience in defending doctors. There are all sorts of quirks associated with these policies. At the very least you need to address the following matters:

- **Can you choose your own lawyer, or will the insurance choose?** If they choose a dud, you are stuck with inadequate defense.
- **If they want to settle, will they ask you for permission?** And if you deny it, will they continue to defend you or will they tell you you're on your own?
- **If you lose the first trial, will they continue defending you until all means of appeal have been exhausted?** You may lose the initial trial, but still think you did nothing wrong and want an appeal. That is your right under the law. However, the right cannot be exercised if you have pay for your own defense. Very likely, you cannot afford it anyway.
- **Can they cancel your policy whenever they want?** To my knowledge, there are some legal restrictions on how fast an insurance can dump you. However, it is a definite possibility and it depends on state law.

Asset protection

This is a buzzword that circulates among doctors like a vulture over a dead horse. The concern is the following: if you lose a suit and the award against you is in excess of your insurance coverage, you are up the creek. You stand to lose your house (assuming it is truly yours and not mortgaged), your money, your stamp collection and the shirt off your back. However, in my opinion and to the best of my knowledge, this is a very unlikely scenario. I discussed the issue at length with a reputable defense lawyer. He told me this is not a worry you need to have, because awards rarely exceed the coverage amount. He believes this happens so rarely, that you don't need to lose any sleep over it. After all, the patient and his lawyer will go after the "easy money" which is your coverage, not the money you may have stashed away in a foreign trust. However, I insert a disclaimer: **this is strictly my opinion.** You must do your own homework on this subject and arrive at your own conclusion.

If you are worried you could lose your assets in a suit, here is what to do about it:

- **Determine exactly what assets are at risk.** Some are, some are not. The money in your checking account is at risk, the money in the IRA is not, at least to my knowledge.
- **Determine how much of a chore it would be to protect the assets at risk.** You would need to talk to a reputable lawyer, with experience in the field. They are hard to find.
- **If it is a big chore, especially if it is very expensive, strongly consider buying more (malpractice) insurance, rather than going through asset protection gymnastics.** It may very well be cheaper, easier to understand and it is a deductible practice expense. Asset protection per se is not a recognized business expense!

PEARL OF WISDOM

In all my dealings with this issue, I found **the field of "asset protection" to be a swamp of bad advice, avaricious lawyers, expenses, complications and confusion.** It is an extremely complex subject, far beyond the scope of this book. It is also, completely beyond beginners. Don't simply go to a lawyer and ask him to "protect your assets". That is utter folly. **You must study the issue yourself very carefully first, read books, think about it with your feet in cold water before you make a move.** There is no such thing as an "asset protection emergency", although many lawyers tell you to "act now, not tomorrow". This must be approached very methodically and carefully. You must know enough about the subject to follow a conversation with an "expert" lawyer. You must be able to tell good advice from bad one. However, **THE FIRST STEP IS TO DETERMINE IF YOU HAVE ASSETS AT RISK. IF YOU DON'T, OR IF YOUR ASSETS ARE SMALL, STOP WORRYING ABOUT THIS ISSUE!**

CONCLUSIONS

You will be sued. Obviously, not every single doctor gets sued, but enough of us to make it a very high probability. The time to prepare for a suit is now! Ignoring the issue is like sticking your head in the sand. Here is a summary of how to prepare, in no particular order of importance:

- **Understand that suits happen and prepare yourself psychologically for that moment.** I often hear doctors felt "devastated" by a suit. I never understood why. You knew it would happen, why are you devastated?
- **Don't do business with doctors known to testify against their colleagues.** For example, don't give them referrals. As discussed, the habitual expert witness (for the patient!), would likely not hesitate to testify against you too. Therefore keep these people at arm's length.
- **Write defensible notes consistently.**
- **Cover your ass.**
- **Buy sufficient insurance.**
- **Understand how malpractice insurance works, what it can do for you and what it will not.**
- **When in doubt, when you are sued, go to trial rather than settling.** This, of course, assuming you did not do something completely boneheaded, like cutting off the wrong leg.
- **Watch your defense lawyer very carefully during a suit.** Remember, it's your ass, not his. You must insist on excellent defense. You paid for it already with your insurance premiums. If you doubt the lawyer's skill, make noise and ask for a better one.
- **Understand that you cannot trust your patients.** It pains me to say that, but it is an inevitable conclusion. Again, this does not mean you should be a ding-dong doc. Give them your best, but forget about being friends with them.
- **Take a proactive role in your defense.** Don't just sit there and take anything thrown at you, hypnotized like a rabbit looking at the snake that's ready to eat it. If someone gets in your face, tell him to buzz-off.
- **Fight the concept of "standard of care" anytime you hear about it.** Point out that there is no such thing. Point out it is breached every day anyway. Point out that doctors in other countries enjoy "freedom of treatment". Why shouldn't we too? After all, if we're living in a global village, we should learn from our neighbors and profit from what we've learned.
- **Never testify against a doctor in a malpractice suit.** Don't try to solve the issue of tort single handedly. The question of how much (if anything!) should be paid to an injured person is an issue for the

entire nation to debate and solve. It is not for the doctors to solve. Medical malpractice is a very small slice of a much bigger issue.

- **Testify <u>in favor</u> of colleagues who were sued by patients.** Remember, it could happen to you anytime. You would be providing a truly valuable service and you can make money too.

After reading this chapter you finally understand! Now you will never whine again about your malpractice misery. Now you know the doctors did it to themselves. What we did, we can undo. Get to work on it!

Chapter 8: BUSINESS STRATEGIES, THE BASICS

Motto: "Time is money", said the waiter and added the date to the check.

The office manager: meet the person who makes or breaks your practice!

The most naïve thing I ever heard on practice management was this: "Doctor, concentrate on practicing good medicine and the rest will take care of itself". I consider this statement to be so monumentally misleading as to merit its own board exam question! Somehow, miraculously, insurance plans will offer you good contracts. The rent will pay itself. Personnel will be hired and supervised. Right! The reality is **NOTHING WILL TAKE CARE OF ITSELF. NOTHING AT ALL!** You have to take care of everything yourself. You have to learn to be a businessman to succeed as a private practitioner. Therefore, the practice manager, the person who runs it day-to-day, makes it or breaks it.

PEARL OF WISDOM

The ideal practice manager is someone who has a financial interest in the business. I believe this statement applies to most small businesses. It is no coincidence that many small shops are "mom and pop" stores. Think of how many bakeries, bed and breakfast places and restaurants you've seen that were run by a married couple!

The ideal manager could be:

- **A close relative,** for example a spouse. But careful! Your marriage must be strong enough to stand this an additional burden. I am my wife's practice manager. I have been asked, "How can you stand to work with your wife every day?" The question is not about **my** wife in particular, but rather "how can anyone stand to work with his wife?" Well, I can stand my wife just fine. However, before you "hire" your spouse to manage your office, make sure it is feasible! I don't advocate sacrificing your marriage to manage an office. There is another detail to keep in mind: the staff may not like having a married couple as a double boss. After all, if the receptionist doesn't like the office manager, who is he going to complain to?
- **You!** Yes, you can be your own office manager. This has the additional advantage of not having to pay one! However, just like the

thing with the spouse, this has to be done right to succeed. Remember, you must make time <u>every day</u> to attend to your managerial duties. Time away from patient care. Most likely this means either closing the practice early, or closing it for 2-3 hours around lunch time. The practice must be closed in my judgment, for you to attend to its management. Otherwise the phone will ring, patients will walk in and before long you'll find yourself writing prescriptions during the time you were supposed to go over the billings. If that happens, disaster has occurred. Managerial duties cannot be neglected. I would go even further than that: it is preferable to have a smaller practice managed by you than a big practice managed by a hired hand. To manage your practice yourself, you must have time to do so. If you are running a full office, you will not have time! But wait a minute, the attentive reader will say: if your practice isn't full, you are making less money compared with a full practice. Yes, this is true, but you don't have a very big expense either. You don't need to pay an office manager. You are managing it yourself. In that case, you can afford to have less income, because you have fewer expenses. Good practice managers are very, very expensive!

The case against the hired manager

Theoretically, you could find an experienced and dedicated manager for hire. Such people do exist. This person could be your watchdog and run the office for you. However, the question is **WHO IS WATCHING THE WATCHDOG?** Typically, the doctor looks after his own duties, sees patients, writes notes, **and forgets to supervise the manager!** This is like allowing a pilot to leave his seat half-way through the flight, hoping the plane will land itself somehow. Practical experience shows that an office manager will work only as hard as needed to keep his job. If you hire a manger and fail to supervise him, you've wasted your money. You might as well not hire him in the first place! All businesses must have someone watch the watchdog. Otherwise Enron happens!

A typical scenario would be the following:

A solo medical practice finds a good manager. The manager takes his duties seriously and provides the doctor with regular feed-back. The manager expects the doctor to make crucial, strategic and tactical decisions based on the information presented. That is the job of the owner. However, instead of meeting with the manager regularly, the doctor sees patients. In the doctor's mind, it is far more important to see patients, instead of poring over the "accounts receivables", because seeing patients brings in the cash. When he sees patients the doctor fulfills his role as "worker". However, as discussed in previous chapters, worker is not the only role for the doctor. He is also owner. As owner, he must supervise the manager. All managers must be supervised. Why? Because otherwise they either slack-off or engage in all sorts of "creative" activities like giving themselves bonuses, large salaries, perks and so on. For details, see the recent cases on Enron, World-Com, and Citigroup. Let's go back to our solo practice and see what happens next:

- **The doctor fails to meet with the manager regularly.** A manager will try to schedule meetings with the doctor only so many times. If the doctor does not seem interested, the manager will no longer bother to keep the doctor informed of what is going on in the practice. Or worse, the manager himself stops keeping on top. I can't tell you how many times I talked to hired managers and asked key questions only to be told "I don't know". "How much is the rent?" "I don't know" "Are you contracted with insurance X" "I don't know" "How much of your accounts receivables are >90 days?" "I don't know". These are managers who have stopped working a long time ago. Why? Because they can get by with minimum effort. Nobody is checking on them. If they don't do their jobs, why pay them? Very likely these were very good managers, but human nature being what it is, they soon "adapted", they only put in as much effort as necessary to keep their jobs. This is far less than necessary to run the office well!

- **The doctor meets with the manager, but doesn't know hot to interpret the data presented to him.** Since the doctor will never admit to being clueless, he will just muddle through. The problem in this case is that the doctor never took the time to learn how to think as a businessman. He believes all he has to do is be a good doctor and the rest will simply take care of itself. For example, the office manager may show the distribution of the accounts receivable to the doctor. The doctor may not even know what "receivables" are, much less if the graph is good news or bad news for the bottom line.

- **Cost control is a foreign word.** Since hired managers are just that, simple employees whose pay comes in regularly, they rarely take a businessman's look at costs. You, the doctor must make the manger take a hard look at where you buy your supplies, whether you are charged unreasonable expenses, or whether you really need all the personnel you have. Cost control is a vital matter for a small business and it is discussed below.

- **The doctor fails to override the manager when he makes mistakes.** One of the biggest issues is excess personnel. Remember, the more people you mange, the higher your status in the management world. A guy who runs a 5 man operation is a lot lower on the totem pole of business than one who runs a 50,000 man operation. Consequently, guess what? Managers have a tendency to hire people! "Doctor, I don't know how we can possibly last another day without a second receptionist!". However, to override the manager, you must be a better businessman than the manager. This goes back to my original question why you hired a manager in the first place instead of managing your practice yourself?

- **The doctor hands over the entire operation to the manager.** This happens all too often. The manger becomes so big, nobody dares to supervise him, not even the doctor. I visited an office once and noticed that a nurse had been idle most of the day. I asked the doctor why he felt he needed this employee at all. He told me that all decisions are made by the manager and he (the owner!) does not feel comfortable interfering. Well, you might as well hand over the wallet, the watch, the lunch and the wife too!
- **The doctor allows the manager to sign checks for him.** As in: the manager now signs his own paycheck! What can I say? Maybe some hallelujahs and may this practice rest in peace!

PEARL OF WISDOM

The biggest expert in your office needs to be...YOU! You need to be:

- **The best office manager in the office.** As you see from the examples above, you must know how to manage your office. There must not be any "mysteries" and things unknown to you. To be your own office manger, you need to know your business inside out. If you are going to hire a manger, you need to know it inside out to supervise the manager effectively. Since you need to be the best office manager in the practice, why not be the only one too? Don't hire somebody, do it yourself.
- **The best biller in the office.** The biller handles your cash. The billings need to be done picture perfect. There is no alternative to this. In addition, as discussed before, you need to understand how much money you can expect to make from each procedure you do. Consequently, you must be intimately familiar with all aspects of the billing process. You must be a first rate coder, know how to read the EOBs, when and how to dispute incorrect bills, and so on. It is impractical to enter and send the bills yourself. It is necessary to hire a biller. And it is vital to supervise the biller closely.
- **The best nurse, receptionist, computer expert and purchasing agent.** Again, the reason is you must supervise these employees effectively. How are you going to write a nurse's evaluation if the nurse's duties are unknown to you?

Just how exactly are you supposed to become such and expert manager, coder, biller, nurse and computer geek? The answer is this:

YOU MUST MAKE A HABIT OF DOING EVERYBODY'S JOB, PERIODICALLY. Do some scheduling (yes, it is ok to answer your own phone!), purchasing, billing, injections, sterilizing, etc. You don't need to spend a whole day doing it, just enough time to keep your feet wet. This has another benefit: if any employee quits unexpectedly (and boy, do they love to do that!), you can do that particular job yourself until you find replacement. At least until you can reorganize the office.

When am I going to see patients?

I hear you asking, "If I am supposed to do all these chores around the office and also manage it, when am I going to see patients?" No, it isn't easy.

- **Being in private practice is not a nine-to-five job.** Not initially, at least. However, my experience shows that well organized docs can run their practices efficiently and still go home before midnight. Well before midnight.
- **If you are going to be your own office manager you must make time for this.** It has to be time away from seeing patients. There is no alternative. However, it is better to have a smaller practice managed by you, than a large one managed by a hired hand. Yes, you will have less time to see patients. Your income will be less, but you will make up the loss by eliminating a big expense. In fact, your net pay may be higher.

Who are your clients?

Now that we determined who is running your office, let's see who the clients are. The answer may seem obvious. It's the patients! However, I want to discuss some of the less obvious issues. The correct answer depends on your specialty. For a family doctor, the clients are the entire population in the area where the office is located. Since the general practitioner sees the young and the old, the urgent and the routine, his potential clients are truly the entire population in a particular area. However, for a neurosurgeon the primary clients are not his patients. His primary clients are the doctors who referred the patients to him. After all, nobody walks off the street into a neurosurgeon's office. All patients are referred by another doctor. The area from which the patients are drawn may very well be the entire state, or an even larger area. The point is, you need to understand very well where your patients come from. Why? Because you want more of them and you must know where to find them to lure them in. Not only that, but you may want to tailor your services to the needs of your clients. For example, if you are located near a residential area, you may want to offer extended hours to allow families with children to come to you after school. Or, if you offer a cosmetic procedure, you must locate your office in a high income area. It is pointless to offer $5000 hair transplants if your office is in a working-class neighborhood. Think belly-button piercing instead!

What is your product?

Remember what I told you earlier? All businesses have products. Yours is the advice you give to the patients and the procedures you perform. It is important to understand your product; over the life-time of your practice you will need to adapt the product to the expectations of your clients. For example, you may want to teach a diabetes class, or start doing screening flexible sigmoidoscopies, or keep your practice open late one evening a week. It is important to reexamine these two issues periodically: who are your clients and what is your product? Periodically, think about what you offer and to whom. And if you decide you don't want to make any changes, it is an important conclusion too. However, it should not arise out of inertia. You must first think hard. If, after thinking, you conclude everything is as it should be, by all means, leave everything alone.

Advertising

It has been said that a happy patient will tell three others, but an unhappy one will tell ten others about it. Is it true? Who knows! The point is, patients talk to each other! You should use this to your advantage.

- **Spread the word, dear patient.** Word-of-mouth is undoubtedly a very effective way to find new patients. And the cheapest. Serve your patients well and they will sing your praise. I see nothing wrong with asking your happy patients to tell their friends and families about you.
- **Put a sign somewhere where it can be seen.** If your office is in a strip-mall, make sure the public knows you are there. Put a sign by the side of the road. List your name in the list of businesses.
- **Newspapers.** My neighborhood has a newspaper called "The Tattler", which is thrown into all driveways once a week. Put an advertisement in it! Many neighborhoods have their own versions of "The Tattler".
- **Give speeches.** Where? To answer that, you must first analyze who your patients are. If they are church going types, give a diabetes talk after service.

- **Visit your referring doctors.** If you are a gynecologist who lives in the same medical building with a family doc, visit him and ask him to send you patients. Make sure you send timely consultation reports back to the FP to keep him in the loop.
- **Get on the relevant insurance lists.** They all get updated periodically. Make sure you are listed, especially if you are a generalist whose patients may very well chose you simply because you are in their insurance book and your office is near their work place.
- **Get in the yellow pages.** But only if you are a generalist. Remember, nobody chooses a cardiovascular surgeon from the yellow pages.
- **Have a website.** This should definitely pass the cost control department first. If your patients would rather eat anchovies than use a computer, don't bother with this, at least not yet. There may be a time coming where truly "everything" is online. However, presently, a website is not a requirement for a doctor's office.

Advertising is effective, but can be time consuming not to mention expensive! I would advise you to institute the cheap measures first, like asking patients to bring in their friends.

Common sense

During medical school and residency you were often told to use your common sense. Once you are in private practice, please continue using it. It is priceless. Business and logic are not mutually exclusive. All your decisions should pass the common sense test. To see how it works, let's examine some examples.

- **Doctors with several offices.** You make money by seeing patients. You cannot see patients in several places at the same time. What is the point of having more than one office? If you are an ultra-specialized specialist (retina surgeon? pediatric oncologist?), you may need to open more than one office to cover a big spread-out city like Phoenix. However, do you math carefully. Having two offices means you pay twice the rent. Will you make it up? Ideally, you should only rent for the days you are actually use the office, like a hotel room. Let's say you are in location A Mondays - Wednesday s and in location B Thursdays and Fridays. Maybe you can find another ultra-specialized specialist who will share with you. But if you are not an ultra specialized specialist, common sense says you should have one office only.
- **Doctors with ancillary personnel, for example PAs.** We talked about this in previous chapters, but it is time to revisit the issue. Don't hire a PA if your math shows no increase in your profit. Like I said be-

fore, hiring a PA may be very reasonable, but it should not be a reflexive decision. If you have too many patients, consider decreasing your work-load, rather than increasing your personnel. For example, decrease the number of patients you see by canceling the slow and low paying insurance contracts.

- **If you do hospital work, limit your admissions to one hospital and rent an office on campus.** Rounding at four hospitals before you go to the office is a major waste of time. You don't get paid for traveling, therefore limit the time you spend in the car. Another issue to consider is the "no-doc" ER call. The more hospitals you go to, the more ER call you'll likely have. That's not good!

- **Group practices often don't work.** My personal experience shows that "small is beautiful". When in doubt always go for a solo practice. It is a lot easier to set up, run and make profitable. If there are several docs who think they might work well together, my advice would be to open solo practices and have informal agreements about referrals and cross coverage. You may even share an expensive piece of equipment, if necessary. But stay away from the group practice business model. It has failed so many times, it may fail in your case too.

- **Friendship and business don't mix.** It is a mistake, in my judgment, to go into business with your friends. There is no faster way to ruin a friendship than to squabble over money. Remember, if a friend steps on your toes, you can simply ignore him for a while. A friend who is also a business partner cannot be ignored. You run into him every day. If you have five doctor friends with whom you would like to cooperate, by all means do so. But keep your own business entity and keep an arms-length distance. The reverse is also true: don't confuse a pleasant business partnership with friendship. They are not the same thing. There is a lot of truth in the old mafia saying: "I killed you for business reasons, it wasn't personal!"

- **Doctors who want to keep growing.** In Phoenix, every few years some doctor or another develops visions of grandeur and wants to take over his specialty. He simply wants to be **IT**, i.e., get all doctors of his specialty under his tutelage. None have succeeded. Remember what I said in previous chapters; doctors' offices are not under pressure to "grow" to remain viable. Once you have a full practice, see that you keep it full and stop dreaming about becoming the Microsoft of your specialty. You have neither the capital nor the business knowledge for such an endeavor. Nor are the other doctors going to cooperate! Sooner or later, you will run into egos just as big as yours. You could run into me, for example!

Cost control

For a small business like a medical practice, cost control is not "just" very important. It is a matter of survival. Once you are in private practice, your middle name changes from "W" to "Costcontrol", a name you will never shed! Cost control permeates all aspects of your activity. Did you hear me? **Cost control permeates ALL aspects of your activity!** None of your expenses should be paid without thinking how you can lower them. The reason is this: the money you make is the difference between your income and your expenses. It is very difficult to increase the income. Therefore, always try to lower the expenses. I consider everything that costs more than $ 20 to be an important expense! Turn every dollar around three times before you spend it. Always ask your vendors how you can get a better price, or at least a temporary discount. And always look around you: do you really need three telephone lines, four nurses, five computers, six beepers and seven exam rooms? At the end of each business year I look very carefully at the list of expenses. I examine every item and compare the amount spent this year with the amount spent last year. I ask myself "is this expenses really, absolutely, unavoidable?". Let's look at some examples:

- **Answering service.** What do these guys do anyway? They page you. Get rid of them. Instead have an answering machine at the office telling the callers "the office is closed, if you need urgent attention call 123-4567 (i.e., your beeper)", or the office of the doctor on call for you. That is exactly what the answering service does, for $60 a month.
- **Transcriptions.** Get rid of those too and use a computerized record keeping system instead. It is far, far cheaper.
- **Personnel.** Do you need all these RNs, secretaries, filers and X-ray techs in your office? "I need a nurse to bring back the patients and take their vitals". Really? I don't think so! Why can't you bring back your patients yourself? After all you know when you are ready to see the next patient. Do your own vitals, rather than pay someone $13/hour plus payroll taxes.
- **Equipment.** Please don't buy that $ 10,000 office management software! Use a word processor instead.
- **Telephone lines.** They are expensive, about $50/month. Do you really need 5 of those? Maybe 2 are enough.
- **Rent.** It is nice to live in the posh part of town, but guess what? Insurance reimbursement is the same in all neighborhoods. Rent will be higher, but will income also be higher?

The service to your clients

If you want to know how well your office is organized approach it from the point of view of your patients. It is very important to place yourself in their shoes and look at the way you run your operation. Do you like what you see? Would **you** be a patient in your practice or would you find it too complicated. Let's say you are a new patient who wants to make an appointment. In your mind, walk yourself through the process. You are the patient; you decide to make an appointment. What happens next? He calls. Well, who answers a machine or a human? How much time would a new patient need to make an appointment? 10 minutes of punching numbers and following the options given to him by an answering machine, or 1 minute of talking to a receptionist. "Good morning, Dr. Schmendrick's office. Ah, you want to make an urgent appointment? How about coming in now? Great, will see you when you get here; don't forget your insurance card and you co-payment, good bye".

Part one: the beginning. How easy is it for a patient to come to see you? The only correct answer is that it should be as easy as a phone call. Please, please, pretty please have a live person answer the phone! Personally, I find answering machines an inadequate receptionist for a doctor's office. After all, the automatic options guide you to…the receptionist, who should have picked up the phone in the first place! The way your office answers the phone is very important because it is the first impression the patients get of your business. First impressions count. Give the patients a reason to come to you, make it easy to call.

Part two: the middle. Remember, the patients come to you to help them solve a problem. Is the person who answers the phone trained to solve problems? Maybe they want a "physical", which can be a routine appointment; maybe they simply want their narcotics, but they may have something urgent! It does not need to be medically urgent, but if the patient perceives it to be urgent, it is urgent. I had a patient make an urgent appointment because her son had pimple he wanted gone by the week-end, because it was his high-school prom! Since the receptionist deals with these calls first, he should be instructed to solve whatever problem the patient may be calling about. This, of course, to the extent that he is trained to do so. The receptionist should be more than an automaton that answers the phone and then goes off to find somebody who cares.

Part three: the end. The patient comes into your office. What happens once he gets there? Is it easy to sign-in, or is your office giving the IRS a run for the bureaucratic gold medal? Is the waiting room a dump or a nice, relaxing place? Are there magazines to read? How long is the wait going to be? If it is long, come out and tell the patient yourself! Incidentally, I see more and more waiting areas equipped with TV sets. Personally, I find them most irritating. I imagine others do too. Don't jump on the latest fad, simply because every other doctor did. There are things that don't belong in a doctor's waiting room, and a TV blaring commercials is definitely among them.

Part four: the epilogue. After the patient leaves, what happens next? If you did some tests, will you call him yourself with the results? How soon?

PEARL OF WISDOM

If you want to know how well you run your office, approach it from the point of view of the patient. In your mind follow some typical scenarios:

- **Patient calls for a routine appointment.**
- **Patient calls for an urgent problem.**
- **Patient left your office with a referral to specialist.** Did you remember to give him a paper referral if so required by his insurance? Did you give him the specialist's business card, instructions what to do after he sees the specialist, a follow-up appointment with you? If it is urgent, did you call the specialist yourself and make an urgent appointment on behalf of the patient?
- **Patient had a routine blood test done in your office.** Are you going to call him with the results? When?
- **Patient had an urgent test in your office, for example a rapid strep screen .** Are you going to call him with the results before you go home that day?

Chapter 9:
DIVERSIFICATION AND ADVANCED BUSINESS STRATEGIES

Motto: Washing alone is not enough.
Sometimes you need to change the water.

Diversification

It is important to make yourself familiar with the concept of diversification. What does it mean and how will it help your business? Let's say you are a family practitioner. Your obvious main line of business is seeing sick patients, or screening (annual physicals, school physicals, pap smears) However, relying on a single "product" is not good business. Your revenue will fluctuate from year to year. There will be good times and bad times. That's the nature of business. During bad times it is important to have something else to fall-back on for additional income. Here is what to do:

- **Sign up with many insurance companies, not with just a few.** For a doctor, this is the first step towards diversification. You don't want to depend on just a few insurance plans. I see this all the time: offices where most income comes from a single payer. The "Aetna practice" as it were. If that particular insurance catches a cold, you catch an autopsy!
- **Procedures.** It is very important to learn procedures, because the pay is a lot higher for procedures than for "brain" work, such as pondering a differential diagnosis. Learn to remove moles, lipomas, fix torn ears from ripping ear rings, flexible sigmoidoscopies, etc. If you did not learn it in residency, it will be difficult later and expensive. Consequently, learn as many procedures as you can during residency. It is the most important step towards diversification because procedures have always been and will always be better paid than brain work.
- **Cosmetics.** Past experience shows that the patient who moans about paying a $ 25 co-payment for a sore throat will not hesitate to spend his entire tax refund on a cosmetic procedure! The reason why you should consider learning such procedures is that they are always performed for cash collected upfront. No need to bill an insurance, wait for payments and deal with disputes. Notice I said "cash", because that is exactly what you will ask for. Do not fall into the trap of offering "payment plans". You are not a bank.

It is the patient's problem to find the dough for his nose job!

- **Testify in favor of your colleagues in malpractice suits.** You should never testify against your colleagues, anyway. But you certainly should do so in favor of doctors who got sued. Lawsuits will never go away, so being an expert witness can be a good source of income. Hook-up with several defense lawyers and offer your services as an expert witness for doctors who were sued. This is the closest you will ever come to "money for nothing". It is very easy work compared with doctoring, yet it is very well paid.

- **The wellness thing.** This is a very broad category, but it seems to be a profitable fad. Do wellness evaluations for cash.

- **House visits.** There I go again, but my nose tells me there is money to be made here. Again, you would ask for cash upfront, instead of billing an insurance. I think the price should be about the same as a co-payment for a visit to the ER. I bet many patients would rather have you come to their house than go to the ER if the price is the same! There are some important points: limit your services to a small and compact geographic area, such as a tight residential area, because you want short driving distances between calls. A few years ago some doctors here in Phoenix wanted to do house visits and cover the entire city. Complete with 800-numbers and a large van with a mobile laboratory in it. I think this is the wrong way to go about it. The city is simply too big to cover. Think small and don't buy a lot of expensive equipment like a mobile lab. Make sure the residents can afford your fees. Make sure it is safe for you to wander around in that particular neighborhood. And make sure the population mix is appropriate. Retirement areas and residential areas are prime territory, because the old folks and families with children would profit most from a mobile doc.

- **Hotel doc.** Same concept as house calls. Talk to managers of large resorts and get them to place your business card in the room, for example in the "guest services" brochure. When you see patients, you charge cash upfront, same as with house calls.

- **Teaching.** If you have a special skill, try to become a "professor". My wife does stereotactic breast biopsies. She works as a consultant for the company that makes the biopsy device. Maybe you too have a marketable skill like that.

- **Boutique medicine.** This seems to be the new buzzword. A la prima vista it seems a logical business model, but I have my doubts. Here is how it works most of the time: the patient pays the doctor a flat fee in advance, let's says $ 2,000 a year. For this fee he will have access to special services, such as same day appointments, know the doctor's cell phone number, and maybe even get a house visit or two. Not only does the patient pay an additional fee (additional to his health insurance premium) but the insurance is also billed. It seems the doctor gets paid twice under this system: once via the patient's flat fee and a second time after billing the insurance. The problem with this particular flat fee system is the same as for all flat fee systems: DO THE FEES COVER THE COSTS? I fear that patients who are given special privileges will use them so frequently that they will generate more costs than the flat fee covers. I think this concept has merit, but it is not for the beginner. The key to success is to judge how high the flat fee must be to cover the costs and to generate profit. This can be done, but it is for doctors who have been in business for a while. You must know your patients very well to, because you must make a prediction about how often they will use the services covered by the flat fee. A word of caution: if you are considering becoming a boutique doctor, you need to obtain legal counsel on how your plan complies with Medicare rules and with general ethical standards. After all, if you award your retainer-patients special privileges, you are creating two classes of patients, namely those who can afford them and those who cannot. Is that legal/ethical? Have a good lawyer look it over first.

- **The cash-only practice.** This is a practice that does not bill insurances. The patient is charged cash upfront and given a receipt. Afterwards, the patient gets reimbursed by his insurance. In my judgment, this business model is promising and should be considered by every doctor. Naturally, not all specialties are suited for it. A neurosurgeon cannot possibly hope to have nothing but cash paying patients, since his surgeries are very expensive. However, a family doc, or an owner of an urgent care center could very well adopt this modus operandi and succeed. The biggest advantage is that you don't need to do any billings, which saves you big money. No need for expensive billing software, no need to hire a biller! I think that if you set your fees close to the average copay for an ER visit (e.g., ~50-75 bucks), the patients will find it affordable.

- **The internet.** Many new technologies can be exploited for profit. I think the internet can too. For example, you can allow patients to make appointments on-line, or send you their questions via e-mail. You could communicate lab results to them via e-mail too. The key is to make sure security is air tight. After all, when you receive an e-mail asking you to discuss a syphilis screen, you must be certain you are talking to the real patient and not to his wife or employer! The second question is how to bill for this. Do you ask for money first, before you answer an e-mail? Can you bill an insurance for diet advice given on-line? The internet is simply too new for al these questions. I predict that the internet will play a big part of tomorrow's medical practice once the population at large becomes familiar with this technology. I imagine it was the same when the telephone was invented. It took some time before every Hans and Franz could call for pizza delivery.

- **The no-appointment-needed practice.** I saw several of those here in Phoenix. Interestingly, one of them offers house-calls too! In the past, the no-appointment system was more prevalent than now. It seems it is making a come-back. Here is how it works: you do away with all appointments. Instead, you tell your patients to simply come in. They will be seen in the order in which they arrive, unless there is an emergency. The patients must be willing to wait until their turn comes. The wait could be an hour or more. The waiting time depends on the complexity of the patients you care for. If you have five train wrecks in a row, the sixth patient must be willing to wait quite a long time. To make this a success several things need to happen. The patients must accept this system and not mind waiting. You must limit the hours when patients can come in. For example, you open at 8:00 and you keep the door open until 11:00. Your pledge to the patients would be, "Walk in between 8:00 and 11:00 and I will see you that morning". Then close the door until 14:00. During this time you don't let anybody in. That gives you time to catch up, see all the patients who arrived that morning and get lunch. Then do the same in the afternoon. Open at 14:00 and close at 17:00. Let the patients know that if they walk in during those hours, they will be seen that afternoon. You and your staff must be willing to stay as long as needed to see all patients who walked in. The advantage is that you can do away with the receptionist, since there is no need to call for appointments. This saves you a full time employee. The disadvantage is that the patients would need to wait a long time to be seen. You must know your patients very well before you spring this system on them. Nowadays everything runs on appointments, even Supercuts! Perhaps times are changing and people will accept a new system, "Come in without calling first and wait to be seen".

Remember: if you branch out into a new line of business, **it must be profitable.** You may enjoy doing cosmetic procedures, but do you make money from them? You are going to have start-up expenses, for example equipment, courses you may need to take and advertising. In my judgment, you should recoup these costs within a year and be profitable during the 13th month. Otherwise you miscalculated.

Some of the newer business models for medical practices involve getting paid upfront for services you will render later. Many other businesses do this. Think of airlines, who offer discounts if you buy your ticket far in advance. However, in my judgment, all these models are for experienced businessmen, not for beginners. How does an airline calculated its advance-purchase discount? Should it be 60% if you buy 3 months in advance, 30% if you buy 1 month in advance, or what? It is not easy to make these calculations. Yet they must be correct, otherwise you will find that the money collected upfront does not cover the expenses generated later.

PEARL OF WISDOM

Every single aspect of your business must be profitable. For example, if you are a family practitioner and you do hair implants on the side, both activities must be profitable. Don't finance your cosmetic procedures with money you make from your "regular" patients. If your cosmetic procedures are not profitable, either fix it, or stop doing it!

Renegotiating insurance contracts.

Imagine you have been in practice a few years and are doing well. Now it is time to look at your insurance contracts. Most certainly there will be some you would rather not deal with. Don't hesitate to cancel contracts which did not live up to their promise. **This, of course, assumes your practice is large enough to absorb some loss of clients.** For example:

- **Low payers.** Look at reibursement for some typical procedures: new patient visits, physicals, mole removals, etc. Your billing software will provide a summary of payments broken down by insurance. The lowest payers need to be addressed. Call them and ask for a raise. Be polite, but also show them your stick, namely your willingness to cancel the contract. If they don't budge, cancel!
- **Slow payers.** Same as above, except you may want to save yourself the effort of calling them. Remember, slow payers are not likely to speed-up simply because you yell at them. Very likely they are too incompetent to process the bills in a timely manner. Alternatively, the slow payers may be slow because they lack the money to pay the doctors. In that case, you must cancel your contract pronto! If they run out of money, you will never be paid. Insurances go belly-up too and you don't want to be caught holding a worthless IOU!

Business intelligence

As a businessman you must be forever watchful and constantly collect information about your environment. Examples include:

- **Watching the competition.** This is mandatory. Know who your competitors are and keep an eye on them. What? You did not even know you had competitors? You make a habit of being nice to everybody. You don't think there is competition among doctors? Time for a reality check! Think about it this way: do you want patients to come to you, or to other doctors in your specialty? See? there is competition. Watch the other practices and see how they do business. Call and see how easy it is to make an appointment. Constantly engage your colleagues in conversation. Maybe you can learn something. Even finding out that you don't want to change anything is important intelligence.
- **Hiring practices of other doctors.** How much staff do your colleagues have? If it seems like they have too many or too few employees talk to them and see how they justify it.
- **How is reimbursement by insurance plans?** Knowing the general lever of reimbursement allows you to gauge how well you did in your latest contract negotiations. But careful! Most doctors don't have a clue how much they get paid for a particular procedure. Talk such as "I get 200% Medicare" is common. Is it accurate? Not likely. Know what is realistic before you go home and slice open your wrists because you only get 95% Medicare.
- **How much are your colleagues paying their staff?** Know that your staff certainly talks to people working in other doctor's offices. If you find your employees grumble about your pay, look around and see if you have not fallen behind! Perhaps it is time for a pay hike. But then again, perhaps it is not. You need intelligence to answer that question.
- **Who takes call with whom?** If you are on-call too often, can you hook-up with colleagues and lower your call frequency?
- **When colleagues get sued, did their insurance actually help?** Or did it just order them to settle?
- **Which is the cheapest supplier of medical supplies?** You need to buy syringes and gauze, table paper and sutures. Where is the cheapest source?

Read your EOBs (and change the way you practice based on what you learned)

I've told you this before in the chapter on billings, but it needs to be repeated here in a different context. The EOBs will tell you how insurances interpret your charges. For example:

- **Modifier 25.** Let's say you see a patient with a cold, who also tells you he wants a mole removed. Theoretically, you could bill for the cold attach modifier 25 and remove the mole too. In theory, this tells the insurance that a separately billable procedure was done at the time of an evaluation and management (e/m) encounter. Theoretically, you should be paid for both, the e/m code and the mole code. But guess what? Not all insurances see it that way. Some will refuse to pay for an e/m code done on the same day you did a procedure. Knowing this, you tell the patient to come back after his cold is gone for the mole removal. That way, you get paid for both, the e/m encounter and the procedure.
- **Discounts.** If you do more than one procedure on the same day, insurances will pay you their full fee for the first one, and discount the others 50%. Let's say a patient wants you to remove 2 moles. Make him come twice that way you get paid 100% for both moles. If you do them both on the same day, you forfeit 50% of the reimbursement on the second mole. Of course, be careful not to push the patients around too far, otherwise they will leave your practice and you don't get to remove any moles!
- **The most expensive procedure goes first on the HCFA-1500.** Let's say you do 3 moles at the same time. A 5cm one, a 3 cm one and a 2 cm one. Obviously, the biggest mole brings the biggest reimbursement. Therefore, you must put in on the first line of the form. Then the second most expensive procedure and then the third. The reason is that the second and third will be discounted. You don't want your most expensive procedure of the day to be discounted! You want to list it first, so you get 100% of the most expensive procedure and 50% of the least expensive ones.

Chapter 10: ACCOUNTING AND PAYROLL

Motto: Pigs get fat and hogs get slaughtered.

Accounting

Let's cut to the chase: nobody likes to do accounting. It has a reputation of being boring, nerdy, uncool. Unfortunately, it is absolutely vital for your business. Since it is vital, forget about hating it and embrace it. Accounting is a summary of all your business financials. Since it deals with money, it cannot possibly be boring! You have the following options:

- **You do it yourself.** This has been made a lot easier by new accounting software, such as QuickBooks. However, all software assumes that you know how to do it. Just like a word processor will not teach you how to read and write, QuickBooks will not teach you accounting. Teaching you accounting is beyond the scope of this book. Instead, you should do what I did. I sat down with someone who was willing to teach me, for a fee. In my case it was the office manager of the CPA who did my taxes. I did not learn from the CPA himself because he charged more than his office manager. It cost me some money, but it turned out to be money well spent. Now I can do it myself. Not only I can put the correct numbers in the correct column, but I also understand the principles, which is even more important.
- **You farm it out to your CPA's office.** I am against it. I find that if you punch in the numbers yourself, you have a much better feel for your business financials than if you only look at numbers entered by somebody else. Besides, it will cost you!

PEARL OF WISDOM

Accounting must be accurate! Your business is not Enron. You're not trying to pull the wool over anybody's eyes; therefore you must record all financial matters exactly as they are. The only one who will ever look at these numbers is you, so there is no need to be "creative". Be truthful instead.

The accounting data is used for what purpose?

At the end of every business year, you have a very important job. You need to look at your financials and analyze them.

- **Look at all your sources of income.** Let's say your money comes from seeing patients, consulting for a manufacturer of a medical device and from testifying on behalf of other doctors in malpractice cases. Examine all these numbers. How do they look to you? Do you see potential for more income? Maybe you think you worked very hard as a consultant and you only have $ 7,000 to show at the end of the year. Do you want to continue it? Perhaps it would be better to do more defense work in malpractice cases instead, if the pay is better. Also look at how these numbers change from year to year. Are you making as much money from seeing patients as you did last year? More? Less? Is there room for improvement?
- **Look at all the expenses.** All of them. Line by line, category by category. Compare past years with the current year. Ask yourself how you can lower them. Do you really need 3 employees? How about finding cheaper office space? And so on. The important point is to analyze every single expense.

What is a business expense, what is not?

Every dollar spent on your business is a business expense. You must include all possible expenses because they lower your taxable income. I touched on this in previous chapters, but it needs to be repeated here, because there is confusion on this subject. The things to know are:

- **You get back form Uncle Sam only a fraction of your business expenses, never the whole amount.** Never! You only get back an amount proportional to your tax bracket. If your tax bracket is 30%, that is exactly what you get back: 30% of your business expense. A business expense is often called a "tax deduction". This is misleading, because some people think if they spend $ 20,000 on malpractice insurance, their taxes will be lowered by $20,000. No such luck! The $20,000 are deducted from the taxable income. They are not deducted from the taxes.
- **Don't ever buy anything simply because it is a "business expense" and therefore a little cheaper to you.** I said so in previous chapters, but it is important and it needs to be repeated. Instead of spending money, don't. You will end up with more money in your pocket if you avoid an expense altogether, rather than having a deductible expense. Don't ever make the mistake of thinking, "I don't really need this item in my office, but it is a business expense and I will buy it anyway". That kind of thinking leads to financial ruin. Avoid it! Only buy things you really need, never stuff that just

might come in handy some day. Some day never comes, but the expense can never be unmade.

- **Don't tempt fate by including personal expenses as business expenses.** It is very, very tempting to slap all sorts of stuff on your practice expense sheet. Don't. Remember what I said at the beginning of the chapter: pigs get fat and hogs get slaughtered. Be piggish, not hoggish. If you buy a computer for your office and your kid plays pin-ball on it every once in a while, it is a business expense. Theoretically, you would have to calculate the percentage of its use for business and deduct only that. But if you don't, you are still only being piggish. However, if you deduct your two-week sailing trip as a business expense, you are hoggish. Nobody is going to believe that sailing is a necessary business expense. IRS auditors are not stupid, even if they did not go to Harvard Medical School like you did. All questionable expenses must pass your own sniff test. If they smell a little stale to you, they are going to stink to high heaven to the average IRS agent. Remember, this guy is only making a quarter of what you make. He is not likely to forgive you for using creative accounting. He went into this line of work precisely because he gets to take the fat cats down a peg or two. That's how he gets his kicks. Be smarter than him and you'll be ok.

Payroll

Just like accounting, I think you should do your own payroll. You can learn it from your CPA's office, which will cost you some money upfront. But I would not farm this out either. The reason is it keeps you in touch with your business and it reminds you to pay attention to expenses.

- **Your personnel cost more than you think.** The salary is an obvious expense. But you also need to pay the employer's portion of Medicare and Social Security. And unemployment insurance. And worker's compensation insurance. And benefits. Only by doing your own payroll will you get a feel for how much money you actually spend on your employees. When you understand that, you will no longer hesitate to reduce your workforce, whenever feasible.
- **How much time did your employees actually work?** If this is hard to track, you will need a punch clock! There is no way of knowing this, until you start adding up the worked hours. No employee will ever forgive you for paying him less than he was due. To generate accurate paychecks, you need to track the worked hours accurately.

- **You will need to register your business with several Government agencies.** For example, you will need a Federal Employer Identification Number, a.k.a., TIN (Tax ID Number). You will also need other "numbers" from your state. It is beyond the scope of this book to list them all and teach you how to obtain them and how to use them. But you can learn it for very little money from your CPA, just like I did. Once you have obtained all these registration numbers, you never need to go through this process again.

PEARL OF WISDOM

Doing your own accounting and payroll allows you to keep your fingers on the pulse of your practice. This is very important for any small-business man. You have to know what is going on in your office, financially speaking. When you print the summary at the end of the year, there should be no big surprises!

ANOTHER PEARL OF WISDOM

Accounting and payroll are classic activities for the office manager, PROVIDED YOU HEEDED MY ADVICE AND YOU HIRED AN OFFICE MANAGER WITH A FINANCIAL STAKE IN YOUR PRACTICE, LIKE A SPOUSE! If your spouse runs your office, you can turn this stuff over to the spouse, knowing it will be done right. Piggish but not hoggish. I would not give this very important job to a simple hired hand. You will never know if he did it right or not until you took a look at it yourself. By the time you finished examining his work, you might as well do it yourself.

Chapter 11: MONEY MANAGEMENT

Motto: Wisdom is following me, but I am faster!

You have your own practice, you learned how to run it and you are actually making money. How about that?! Now you have dough, but what are you going to do with it? Strange as it may sound, having money brings its own set of problems: **you need to learn how to invest.**

PEARL OF WISDOM: THE SECRET TO SUCCESSFUL INVESTING REVEALED

THE SECRET IS THIS: YOU HAVE TO KNOW HOW TO INVEST WELL ENOUGH, SO YOU CAN MAKE RATIONAL DECISIONS <u>WITHOUT</u> OUTSIDE HELP.

It is absolutely crucial, and I mean **CRUCIAL** that you teach yourself the basics of investing, so you can make your own decisions. If you know nothing about investing and you therefore depend on the "advice" of others, you are done for! There is an army of "investment advisors" out there who are more than eager to tell you what to do with your dough for a fee. And that is exactly the problem: there is a price to pay for this "advice". This price comes out of your profits and it is very, very difficult to make up this loss. Not only that, but the fees charged are not easily discerned! The venality and greed of these "advisors" are very difficult to penetrate for a beginner. It is imperative that you acquire enough knowledge to be your own investment advisor.

It is beyond the scope of this book to teach you how to invest, but you can teach yourself. Start by taking basic investment courses from your local community college. I found these courses have just the right mix of eye opening information and basic knowledge to allow you to make rational decisions without outside help. In addition, read some books. There are hundreds of books on this subject. For you (the non-professional money manager) the only one I truly recommend is "Making the Most of Your Money" by Jane Bryant Quinn. It is the single most important book you can consult as an amateur investor.

MORE PEARLS OF WISDOM: THINGS YOU WILL NEVER HEAR ANYWHERE

Money comes to money

It is not possible to make money out of no money. You must have something to invest. Let's say you have $10,000 and you can read tomorrow's paper today. You notice that the stock of company XY will double overnight. Within 24 hours you make $10,000 (minus expenses and taxes, of course!) in addition to the ten grand you already had. Yippee! It is nice to have such a profit, but it is hardly retirement money. However, if you had $10,000,000 and you make such a killing overnight, then you are talking serious dough! However, you were rich to begin with.

The take home message here is this: the guy who can save $300 a month is not an "investor", but simply a small saver. It is folly for this fellow to behave like he can truly participate in the financial markets. Such participation, a.k.a. "diversification", is reserved for people with much bigger financial muscles. A small saver should concentrate on limiting the risk of losing his money and stop worrying about what the Dow-Jones did on a particular day.

When you invest, you have 3 enemies: greed, taxes and inflation.

You need to understand all three and deal with them head on.

1.   Greed

You always see the guy who made more money from his investments than you, but you don't notice the millions of people who either made less money than you or even lost money. Investment decisions are made with the feet in cold water. They are cold-blooded, rational decisions resulting from knowledge and judgment. They are never hasty, never on impulse and never "emergencies". Understand this very well: **to have a shot at higher returns you must incur higher risks!** This means that if you get greedy (i.e., can't sleep at night because you want those big returns), you increase the risk of losing all your money. Notice I said all your money, not just the potential gains, but also your principal. Also notice I said **a shot** at higher returns. **A shot is not a guarantee!** Many investors behave like taking high risks will automatically lead to high returns, if they only wait long enough. No such luck. When you take high risks, making a profit is a mere option, not a guarantee. That is precisely the reason why such investments are called "high risk". The reverse is also true; it is not possible to take a conservative strategy and secretly hope for big gains. A CD will never yield as much a speculative investment. However, buying a

CD will not result in your losing your shirt!

2. Taxes

No matter how you cut it, half of your income goes to taxes. Remember, there are obvious taxes, such as the income tax you pay the Feds, but also "hidden" taxes, such as reductions in entitlements. There is also the sales tax and the death tax, which is paid on money that has already been taxed (namely by the Feds and State!). This is called double taxation. It is therefore mandatory to examine how you can lower your taxes. This is a complex subject that cannot be dealt with here. In my experience it is very helpful to know as much about taxes as you can stand to learn without going gaga. Here, same as with investments in general, it pays to have a good grasp of the subject, rather than rely on your tax advisor. Personally, after using a CPA for many years, I now do my own returns. Two things helped: the experience I gathered over the years and tax software, such as Turbo-Tax. In the beginning, these tax-help programs were clumsily written and it was best to forget about them and do your taxes by hand. However, nowadays a program like Turbo-Tax can spoon-feed you all you need to know to do your own return. Having your returns at home on your computer also has another very important advantage; you can plug in numbers and see what the tax consequences would be. For example, I am currently looking at starting a retirement plan for my office. I plug the numbers in Turbo-Tax and I can see quickly if it is an advantage or not. A CPA would typically charge hundreds of dollars for doing the same thing. Incidentally, the CPA also uses software, maybe even TurboTax! You should do the same, rather than pay the CPA to do what you can do yourself.

Another word on taxes: the Federal Government is broke. If it were a private company it would have gone out of business by now. By the way, this applies to all industrialized countries, so hold off on emigrating to Italy. The amount of debt incurred by the Feds is so high, that ultimately the Government will have no choice but to raise taxes. Alternatively, the Government could default on its debt. Or it could do both. Therefore, if you chose deferred taxation on your investment instruments (for example by financing an IRA), you may find yourself paying a lot more taxes when you retire than you could have predicted at this time. This complicates retirement planning quite a bit and it is an additional reason to learn about investing.

3. Inflation

The irritating thing about inflation is that it cannot be avoided no matter what you do. It cannot even be minimized, such as taxes. Consequently, it is very tempting to forget about it altogether. However, you must always count inflation and always count it on the "loss" side. Many, many people act like inflation does not even exist. They forget that all investments shrink every year by an amount equal to the inflation rate. In fact, simply keeping ahead of inflation and taxes is very, very difficult to accomplish for an investor. Let's say you have $100 in your pocket and the inflation rate is 3%. After a year, your $100 shrunk to $97. Of course, it still says $100 on your bill, but it only buys $97 worth of goods. If you invest in something that yields 3% after a year, you have $103 in your pocket. Great, right? Wrong, because, you have not gained anything, you have only kept up with inflation. Please keep in mind, I am talking about AFTER TAXES YIELDS here, meaning that the total yield will have to be quite a bit higher than 3% to beat a 3% inflation rate. Another example: a guy buys himself a house with a 6% mortgage, which he plans to pay off in 30 years. He is happy that interest rates are so low and that he is looking forward to selling it when he retires and live off the profit. This guy is in financial la-la land! It is a classic case of having done only half the home work! His house would have to appreciate in value by:

3% a year to keep up with inflation,
4% a year to keep up with his mortgage and
x% a year to keep up with property taxes, insurance and maintenance.

Notice I did not say 6% a year for his mortgage. Assuming he is in the 30% tax bracket, his mortgage would be reduced by a third (money he gets back from the Feds). Still, his house would have to appreciate by 3 + 4 + x percent a year to brake even. And of course, it would have to appreciate much more than that to be sold as "retirement income". After all, he would have to sell the house to live off the profit. But guess what? If he truly gets lucky and real estate appreciates considerably, then all houses in his community would have appreciated. If he sells his house, he would have to use all the money to buy a new one! To keep his profit he would have to move to a (much!) smaller house, or move to a different, cheaper community. However, the cheaper community is likely to be less glamorous than the one he got used to. Think high crime, rural, or polluted.

The solution to this problem is to pay off the house as fast as possible, rather than stretch it over 30 years. That way, from the moment it is paid off, the house would "only" have to appreciate by:
3% a year to keep up with inflation and
x% a year to keep up with property taxes, insurance and maintenance.

The one thing that will ruin you financially is your house!

A house is an obsession for many people. "I must have a house by this afternoon, or I'll croak!". As a consequence, most families buy houses much too early in their lives and they spend much more than they could rationally afford. The problem with incurring a big expense early in life is you drag it with you for many, many years. In fact, many families I know bought houses that are so expensive, they will die in debt. Yes, you read correctly, the mortgage is so high, they will still owe money on the house when they die! Many don't even have the money to buy furniture for the large houses they live in and spend half their lives in empty rooms. In my analysis, the investment potential of the house you live in is vastly over-rated. The calculations described above show clearly that a mortgaged house is very unlikely to be sold for profit. The way to by a house is this:

- Wait until you know where you are going to work for the foresee-able future. You don't want to buy a house and then find out you will practice in a different city. Buying and selling houses is associated with costs you will never recover.
- Live in a small, cheap rented place until you are sure you'll stay in that community long term.
- During this time, save, save, save, save!
- A $100,000 house may seem like a good deal. However, if you borrow money at 6% and you pay it off over 30 years, the real price of the house will be $ 220,000 ($ 100,000 for the house and $4000 a year x 30 years for the mortgage. Remember, the mortgage is $ 6000 a year, but you get back $ 2000 from the Feds). That is more than twice the listed price. If a house is a good buy at $ 100 grand, at 2.2 x that it is certainly a very bad buy! The calculation above uses a historically low mortgage rate of 6%. However, if you borrow at a higher percentage, the total cost would be astronomical. If you think you will ever recover that when you sell it, you need to wake up!
- Once you save enough money, by all means, buy yourself a house. Should you need to borrow, do not borrow more than 1-2 x your annual after taxes income.
- Don't make the ruinous mistake of buying a palatial home just to show off. Keeping up with the Jones is a major investment no-no! Does anybody really give a rat's ass where you live? Are you the Duke of Tralala who simply has too keep-up a "certain standard"?

Long term does not mean 3-5 years, as you hear in the media, it means life-long!

I find it very amusing when pundits tell their TV audience "you must take the long-term view" and then define "long term" as 3-5 years. An investor with a 3-5 year horizon is a fool! That is much too short. It is not even as long as the average economic cycle! A rational investor's horizon is equal to the rest of his life expectancy, never less. In fact, truly wise investors think a generation ahead. After all, you want to leave some money to your offspring.

In the long term (see above for definition), if you manage to beat taxes and inflation, you have done very well indeed and have every reason to pat yourself on the back.

The point is, have realistic goals. That way you won't feel cheated by life. Don't chase the pie in the sky; don't try to become the next Bill Gates. Trust me, when Gates first learned how to program a computer, he could not have possibly known he would be mentioned in my book in 2004!

Also remember that deferred taxes do not mean taxes will be avoided altogether. In fact you may be in for a nasty surprise! The theory behind tax deferment is that once you retire you will withdraw small sums of money from your retirement funds and thus lower your tax bracket. However, all this planning goes down the drain if the Government raises taxes! In fact, one could very well argue that we are in a low tax period and that future taxes will be higher. The budget deficits of today are the tax increases of tomorrow! After all, the Government debt will not have decreased by the time you retire. On the contrary, it will be so high, that tax increases will be unavoidable. Even in a lower bracket you may very well wind up paying more taxes than if you had taxed your investments now! A guy who invests in taxable instruments (rather than taxed deferred ones) may in fact be the smarter one. Hard to say!

Tune out the noise.

This is eminently important. If you are the type who listens to CNBC, etc., stop. You are not likely to hear anything that will help you personally. Remember, the role of TV talking heads is to entertain you and get you to watch the commercials. They live off gullible clients like you. For reference, see the current scandal about "buy" recommendations by investment banks, recommendations which were put out with the express purpose to generate sales commissions. No matter how this scandal shakes out, the problem will never go away. It is your job to know a conflict of interest when you see one. Don't be gullible, do your homework instead. That way you can tune out the media and not feel like you are missing something.

Be very mindful of hidden fees.

Know they almost always exist. Some investment banks are "honest" and declare all costs up-front. But even then, you need to know to ask about details. For example, when a money market fund costs 0.25% and yields 1.5%, you need to ask "is that yield before or after expenses?" If the expenses have not been deducted yet, do so quickly, in order to get a clear picture of the true yield. After expenses, also deduct inflation and taxes. You may very well find out there is no gain to be made at all!

Be even more mindful of conflicts of interest.

Conflicts of interest take some experience to uncover. Once you suspect such a conflict, ask questions. If the answers do not satisfy you, strongly consider walking away. For example: some years ago, I talked to a "professional investment advisor". The fellow had the required credentials to call himself a "pro". However, in my discussions with him, I noticed that he tried hard to sell me life insurance. All investment proposals he espoused included the purchase of life insurance. His mask was off: this was a life insurance salesman in disguise! This is a very common trick: the "advisor" advises you to buy an investment instrument that generates a sales commission for him. How can you trust such advice? You can't! But you must be knowledgeable and experienced to spot this sort of thing. This does not happen overnight. I recommend you start your life as an investor with a simple, straight forward strategy. After all you did not start your medical career by doing brain surgery. You learned to take the blood pressure first.

Gains are possible, but loses are guaranteed.

Be crystal-clear about this principle. There are no exceptions. Every investor loses money at some point in his life. It is possible to go through a lifetime of "investing" without making any profit at all. But it is not possible to do the same without losses. In bad economic times you may lose money for several years in a row. You must understand that this is unavoidable. No matter how many books you read, how much time you spend watching your money, how diversified you are, how lucky and how clever, you will have to tighten the belt sometimes. Even if you take a most conservative approach, you cannot escape periods of losses. For example, nowadays some investment instruments pay interest rates that are lower than the inflation rate! How are you going to make money in such an environment?

You must have a personal opinion on the economic situation in this country and world-wide in order to make rational decisions on asset allocation.

For this you need solid basic knowledge and you also have to stay current. The weekly magazine "The Economist", for instance is an excellent source for the small investor. An example of "personal opinion" is what I said about the Government being broke and having no choice but to raise taxes. It is based on my thinking that the Government is running deficits because it is unable to control spending. A broke Government will have no choice but to raise taxes to pay for promises made to the electorate.

Asset allocation is the core of all investment.

Unfortunately, it requires considerable judgment, repeat <u>considerable</u> judgment, which, in turn, assumes you know enough about investment to make rational decisions. There are books that tell you something along the line of "you should invest in stocks 100% – your age in years, the rest in bonds and cash". Whoever follows such calculations blindly gets what he deserves. At best these guidelines should spur you to do some reading of your own. If you must ask somebody how to allocate your assets, you are lacking essential knowledge. You must, repeat MUST know enough to make your own asset allocation calculations. This is the core of all investment decision making. If you can't do that on your own, park the money in a low risk instrument (such as a money market fund) and learn how to do it. Asset allocation is a highly personal decision that you should never defer to somebody else.

You cannot learn investment on the fly, you must take a course and do some reading of your own.

If you already have some money and you don't know what to do with it, do not go looking for an "advisor". Being clueless and relying on the advice of others is a recipe for disaster. I'm sure you heard what happens when a guy with money meets a guy with experience; the fellow who has experience winds up with the money and the guy who had the money ends up having an experience. There is no such thing as an investment emergency! Keep the money in a safe place (a savings account, for example) and learn about investing. Afterwards, when you finally have a clue, put what you learned into practice. If you are clueless, learning about investing will take between 1-2 years, depending how much time you have to take courses and read books. It is perfectly ok to leave the money in your savings account while you learn. Rushing to decisions while still clueless is a very bad idea.

Early retirement (for example when you are 50-ish), is very, very, very unrealistic!

The sooner you forget about it, the better. It is much more likely that you will work until you are in your 70s. Why? Because you are not likely to have enough money at age 50 to retire and live off your savings. You would need about 2-3 million dollars (on top of your house, which must not be mortgaged!) to live off the "interest" and you ain't gonna have that kind of dough from a medical practice. Sorry!

If you belong to the middle-income segment of the population (and all doctors do!), the only way to have money is by not spending it.

The only money that truly matters is the money left after expenses, taxes and inflation. I regard the gross income as a sort of "funny money" because it is not yours to spend. Even what is left after expenses is still not yours, because of double taxation (sales tax!). Consequently, **to have money, you MUST CURB YOUR SPENDING**! If you are the kind of doctor who left residency with $60,000 in school loans, then buys a house cum furniture et cum SUV for $500,000, goes on 5 star vacations financed with credit card debt and spends another $150,000 opening a practice, you are done for! You are going to die in debt! A person with so much debt is poor, even if he lives the high-life. In fact, such a man is poorer than a man who only has $10 in his pocket but no debt. The problem with so much debt is that you become a slave to interest payments. This in turn translates to very long hours at the office trying to make money to keep the bill collectors at bay. This in turn translates to high burn-out. Or worse, you begin to "optimize" your income by up-coding, or billing for patients you never saw, i.e., you find yourself driven to theft. I know a surgeon who is 60 years old and has a $600,000 mortgage! At his age it is plain that he will never pay it off. Financially speaking, he is like Keith Richards: dead but does not know it. At 4% a year interest (his mortgage is actually 6%, but the Feds give him a third back, remember?), he has to come up with $24,000 a year just to be allowed to stay in his house. That represents many work hours each year, just to pay the interest. Of course, his inability to curb spending does not stop with the house. He "owns" the obligatory flashy cars (he is a surgeon after all!) and other status enhancing accoutrements. I put "owns" between quotation marks because all this is not really his, since he makes monthly payments. He lives according to the principle "**I buy with money I don't have things that I don't need to impress people I don't like**". Contrast that with a doctor who has no debt. This lucky fellow works a lot less, takes more vacations and has more money in the bank. Burn-out and fraud are not even in his vocabulary. Which one would you like to be?

Also, the guy in debt is in BIG trouble should he get sick. If he cannot work the required hours to pay his bills, he is toast. The slightest wind blowing in his face wipes him out. He will be evicted from his house and office, the cars will be repossessed, and the office staff will leave if he cannot pay them!

Your wealth will come from the money you save, not from the gains made in the financial markets.

As I said earlier, if you are lucky, you will beat taxes and inflation, i.e., the money you saved will keep its value. It is very important you understand that the bulk of your wealth will not come from gains made investing. This is somewhat counterintuitive because you hear so much about spectacular returns generated by certain investments. However, all reported returns fail to subtract inflation, taxes and the costs of investing. When you do so, you will see that many high flying returns are in fact much less impressive, or even...losses! For example, let's say you invest in a mutual fund that yielded 12% last year and inflation was 3%. A handsome return, you will say, as you drive your Mercedes to the country club. Sorry, not quite as handsome, I say. Here is how it works: the 12% are taxed (let's say 30%), which shrinks the gain to 8%. The costs charged by the mutual fund are 1.5% a year. This brings the gain down to 6.5%. Deduct 3% inflation and your total gain is 3.5%. Not bad, since you avoided a loss, but not quite 12%. For those of you who whipped out the calculators, please note the numbers are not meant to be precise; they are only meant to give you the big picture. For example, the costs charged by the mutual fund are likely to be a percentage of the entire sum under management, not just the gain. Please also remember, even if you defer the taxes, you do not avoid them, so deducting the taxes from the yield is a must anyway. Redo the calculations for a 6% yield and you see you actually made a loss!

Double income families must save half their income.

In fact, they should save more than that. The clever ones live on the smaller income and save the larger income. This is easily accomplished if you happen to be married to another doctor, i.e. have two upper middle class incomes in the same family. Please don't tell me you cannot possibly live on "just" one doctor's income! I don't buy that. If you can't, your spending is out of control and you need to reassess your financial situation.

The way to spend a buck.

Let me teach you how to spend a dollar: you take it out of your pocket and you stare at it for a while. After that you turn it around. Then you turn it around some more. After that you turn it around again. And then you put it back in your pocket! The point is: **you don't spend it!**

Chapter 12: CASE DISCUSSIONS
THE BUSINESS MORBIDITY AND MORTALITY CONFERENCE

Motto: Nobody is useless. At least he can be a bad example.

Case 1: To sublet or not to sublet

Part one, the beginning:

Doctor A has been in solo private practice for 1 year. When he opened his shop, a shortage of office space forced him to take a large and expensive office: 1500 sq ft, $ 2700/month. The office has 3 exam rooms and an extra room in the back that is neither used nor needed. The lease is for 3 years.

Doctor B approaches Dr. A and tells him he wants to start an office of his own and is looking to share an office with someone to keep the costs down. He heard Dr. A has an office that is too big for him and wonders if Dr. A would be willing to sublet to him. They have different specialties, so they would not compete against each other.

Part two, the middle:

Dr. A agrees. They also agree that Dr. B will use Dr. A's office equipment and staff, which would save Dr. B quite a lot of money. They agree to a price that includes rent and compensation for equipment and personnel used.

Part tree, the end:

After a year or so, both practices are humming and the personnel are rather busy dealing with patients for two separate practices of two separate specialties. Problems include:

- **Answering the phone** for both practices is cumbersome, since you never know if the patients are for specialist A or specialist B. Each specialty has its own set of problems and the staff finds it difficult to keep abreast of both types of issues.
- Since the costs for personnel are split 50-50, **it is unclear who the supervisor is** and who should write the annual evaluations for the staff. Dr. A thinks it should be him, because he started his practice

a year earlier than Dr. B and the staff was originally hired by him. Dr. B thinks they should evaluate the staff together. He feels that the staff is more accommodating to Dr. A because they view Dr. B as a temporary "guest" who is going to leave and rent his own office sooner or later. Preferably sooner. Dr. B wants to chastise the staff for this attitude and Dr. A does not.

* The lease is up in 1 year and **Dr. A wants to move to a smaller office**, where there would not be room for Dr. B at all. Dr. B feels this would leave him high and dry and in need to find his own digs, staff and equipment. This is an expense he was hoping to avoid altogether, simply by being someone else's room mate forever.

Epilogue: the split.

Dr. A decides to move to a smaller, cheaper office in a year and tells Dr. B he needs to find his own digs and staff. Dr. A thinks a year advance notice is plenty of time. Dr. B reluctantly agrees. After all, what choice does he have? But he is not happy. The final months together are unpleasant.

Analysis

Faced with a shortage of office space, Dr. A had no choice but to rent the big and expensive office when he first went into business. He hoped he would find someone to share rent with and when Dr. B appeared, he was only too happy to sublet.

Correct decisions:

* **Dr. A rents an expensive office** because he had no choice. Prices were up. Alternatively, he could have waited until prices came down, but who knows how long that would take? Also, he could have looked for an office to share, like Dr. B did, but then he would have had Dr. B's problems.
* **Dr. A sublets to Dr. B.** Initially, this was the correct decision, because it lowered Dr. A's operating costs. Dr. B also made the correct decision because he landed in a ready-made nest, not having to buy equipment nor hire personnel.
* **Dr. A charges Dr. B for equipment and personnel.** It is very important to understand that by using Dr. A's equipment, Dr. B is getting a valuable service. For this he must pay his share, for example by participating in the depreciation schedule for the office equip-

ment.

- **At the end of lease, Dr. A moves to a cheaper office.** Dr. A is practicing cost control.

Incorrect decisions:

- **Neither Dr. A, nor Dr. B gave any thought to the question who is going to run the office** and supervise the staff. Dr. A thinks he is the supervisor because he hired the people first. Dr. B's argument is that they should both have a say since the costs are shared. Great, but who has the final say when there is disagreement?
- **Dr. B is wrong to complain about Dr. A's plan to move to a cheaper office.** This does not leave him "high and dry" it just forces him to find his own office, equipment and staff. A good argument could be made that Dr. B should have done so from the start. It would have spared him the conflict with Dr. A and it would have also saved him the need to move to a new office now.

Case 2: I'm looking for a satellite office.

Part one, the beginning:

Dr. A has a full practice in West Anytown metro area. By his own admission, he is as busy as he wants to be and happy with his income. However, lately he has been getting itchy. He wants to "grow". He thinks "growth" should come by "tapping into a different market". He thinks the market to tap into is north-central Anytown, 12 miles away from his current location. When asked why he would want to tap into that particular market (as opposed to another one), he says he thinks that north-central is underserved in his specialty.

Part two, the middle:

Dr. A finds an office to share in north-central Anytown and moves in. The rent is by the hour, which allows him to pay only for time actually spent using the office, with a minimum of 8 hours a week. Dr. A thinks he will easily work 8 hours a week in the satellite office, so he does not think it is a high expense. He already "has a hunch" he will have enough patients to pay for those 8 hours.

Part tree, the end:

This is how it plays out: Dr. A's hunch is correct, north-central Anytown is underserved in specialty and many patients call the satellite office. Much to everybody's surprise, the patients prefer to travel 12 miles to Dr. A's principal office, rather than make an appointment at the satellite. The reason is Dr. A is in the satellite only 1 day a week and the patients want to be seen sooner. Consequently, they are willing to travel!

Epilogue: the satellite is closed!

Seeing that the patients from north-central Anytown come to West Anytown anyway, Dr. A thinks the satellite is no longer needed and cancels his lease.

Analysis

Dr. A is a classic case of "better is the enemy of good". He had a full practice in West-Anytown. What was he hoping to accomplish? A double-full practice? He failed to realize that he can only see patients in one location at a time. By opening a satellite, he increased his costs, but did not increase the income. After all was said and done, Dr. A was exactly where he started out: running a full practice in West Anytown!

Incorrect decisions

- **Wanting a satellite office** in the first place.

Correct decisions

- **Subleasing rather than opening a new office.** This greatly reduced the costs.
- **Reacting correctly to an unexpected development**, namely that the patients were willing to travel to West Anytown. He could not have foreseen this, but once he realized the satellite office is no longer needed, he closed it.

Case 3: I wanna be modern!

Part one, the beginning:

A doctor hears there is a new way of keeping records, something involving computers. Currently he dictates his notes, which are kept in paper folders. He is computer illiterate, but heard that nowadays you can simply speak into a microphone connected to a computer and the computer does the rest.

Part two, the middle:

Since he is computer illiterate, he asks the husband of his office manager (a professional computer programmer) to help. The programmer tells him that voice recognition software is indeed the way of the future, but at present the software is not sufficiently advanced for routine uses, such as writing medical notes. Even in the future, when such software will be commonplace, the doctor would still need to become computer literate to operate it. As an alternative, the programmer suggests using a word processor to write the notes. This, of course, will also require computer literacy.

Part three, the end:

This is how it plays out: the doctor approaches me as a consultant to help him out. He really, really wants to save the cost of transcriptions, currently about $ 500 a month. When I talk to him, his plans summarize as follows: yes, I want to be modern, but I don't want to learn any new skills (I don't have the time), I don't really want to make any changes in the way I do business, and for God's sake, don't tell me you will bring in computers.

Analysis

This guy cannot be helped. He correctly identified the transcriptions as a high and unnecessary cost. However, he failed to follow-through on his observation. He was unwilling to learn new things and introduce modern technology. He would have needed a network of 3 computers in his office, which would have cost him about $3000 including computers, wiring, hub and all labor. This is 6 months worth of dictations. Easily recouped.

The business world, just like medicine, is continuously changing. A business owner must be willing to acquire new knowledge and make changes to his modus operandi. Otherwise he cannot take advantage of productivity gains born out of technological advances. There is no such thing as "I don't have time to improve my shop". This is like saying "I don't have time to make money". If the doctor described above was as busy as he claimed to be, he should have simply closed the office for two weeks; he could have used this time to install and test a computerized record keeping system. Even if he had generated no income at all during the downtime, he would still come out ahead by the end of the year. The cost savings implemented would have paid for themselves in just a few months. However, his biggest problem was that he was unwilling to learn new skills, i.e., become computer literate.

Case 4: I cannot believe this crockery is legal!

Part one, the beginning:

A doctor has been seeing patients covered by Insurance X for many years. During this time there were no problems at all. X is not the highest payer, but not the lowest either. The claims are processed quickly and accurately. Disputes are rare, until one day when the insurance makes a change in reimbursement. The change is made "stealthily" and not announced ahead of time. Claims for a certain procedure are rebundled and reimbursement lowered by $100 per claim. When the doctor disputes the calims, the insurance says it has revised its bundling policies, resulting in a drop in reimbursement by $ 100 for that particular procedure. Funny how bundling policies are rarely revised to result in a pay increase!

Part two, the middle:

The doctor performs the procedure frequently and he feels it is state of the art. Alternatives are less convenient for the patient and also more expensive to the insurance. He does not want to roll over and simply accept this cut in pay. He looks at his contract and discovers that the insurance has indeed the right to change bundling and reimbursement policies any time it pleases.

Part three, the end:

The doctor contacts the insurance and requests a change in the wording of the contract. He also asks for reimbursement for payment withheld. He tells the insurance that if they don't comply with his request, he will no longer offer this procedure to their patients. Instead, he will do a different procedure, which is more invasive and will cost the insurance about $ 2000 more per procedure. Or he will simply no longer see their patients.

Epilogue: we are a 500 pound gorilla!

After going through the motions of listening to his gripes, the insurance tells the doctor to go piss up a rope. After all, the insurance is big and the doctor is small. The insurance evidently feels it has enough doctors on its panel. There is no need to pay any attention to a small doc.

Analysis

The doctor did exactly the right thing. The only way to get an insurance's attention is to hit it where it hurts: in the pocketbook! It is particularly important to show insurances that you are willing to forgo seeing their patients, rather than take a pay cut. This, of course, assumes you are broadly diversified and the loss of any single insurance will not hurt you too much. Now that the insurance showed it true face, the doctor has no choice but to either perform the more invasive procedure or accept a pay cut. This is a difficult decision, because the doctor feels the invasive procedure is no longer state of the art. In the end, rather than perform an inferior procedure, the doctor decides to stop accepting Insurance X. The winner: nobody. The loser: all involved, especially the patients. Does the insurance see it that way? No. Does it care? No. Is it a smart business decision on the part of the insurance? Absolutely not, because all it accomplished was to irritate a doctor and to loose an important service for its patients. All in the name of saving $100 per procedure. Incidentally, if it wanted to save money, it could have just as easily drop reimbursement for that particular procedure, rather than revise the bundling policies. However, decreasing reimbursement would have been a step easily recognized by the doctors. My belief is that the insurance wanted to do this by stealth and hoped to get away with it. Since many doctors do not bother to read their EOBs, many would not have noticed the new bundling. This is a typical example of the sneaky way some insurances try to save money.

Case 5: Canceling an insurance contract

Part one, the beginning:

The doctor in this case has a busy practice, but, unfortunately, it is not diversified. About 50% of his patients are covered by GaGa Insurance. The other 50% come from other smaller insurances. GaGa is not doing well. Its leadership is incompetent, its financials shaky. Payments are regularly delayed for three to four months. The doctor's biller has a chronic headache from dealing with GaGa. The doctor knows personally several members of the GaGa leadership and agrees with common wisdom: incompetence is present! The doctor is very concerned that GaGa will go bankrupt and leave him holding a bunch of IOUs (bills that were sent, but will never be paid).

Part two, the middle:

The doctor recognizes that the only way out is to cancel his GaGa contract. However, he is worried that his income will drop 50%, since currently half of his money comes from GaGa. He wonders what to do.

Part three, the end:

The doctor takes a good long look at all his contracts and realizes that he is not contracted with two of the large insurances in his state. He thinks that by signing a contract with them at the same time he cancels the GaGa contract, he will soften the loss caused by the disappearance of the GaGa patients. In essence, he is hoping to replace the GaGa patients with new ones.

Epilogue:

The doctor puts his plan into action: he signs on with the new insurances and cancels the GaGa contract. It turns out his instincts were correct. The loss of GaGa patients is compensated by the arrival of new ones. The doctor's personal income for the year goes down only 15%, rather than the feared 50%. The doctor decides to absorb the loss by not going on his annual skiing vacation.

Analysis

This example illustrates the importance of diversification. You don't want to become depended on a single insurance for half of the revenue. If that particular insurance catches a cold, you will have a cardiac arrest! No business can afford to lose 50% of its income. This doctor did exactly the correct thing.

Case 6: Let's spend some money!

Part one, the beginning:

Dr. A and Dr. B just finished their residency. They want to open a practice together. They have known each other a few years went through residency together and feel that they could work together in a two-man practice. They put their plans into action and open a practice. They are both computer literate and realize the advantage of a computerized office. Consequently, they buy a practice management software package that does everything: records, billings, appointments, the works. They spend (are you sitting down?) $ 90,000 on this software package!

Part two, the middle:

The package was recommended to them by another doctor, who has been using it for a few years and likes it very much.

Part three, the end:

The software is installed and works well.

Epilogue:

It takes them 3 years to pay off the software, which brings the total cost to (are you still sitting down?) $ 110,000.

Analysis

This is not a big expense. This is not a humongous expense. This is an astronomical expense for a small business. Is it a good idea? If it saves them another big expense, yes. Otherwise not. It saves them the costs of establishing and maintaining paper charts. Does it save them anything else, for example a full-time employee? No. Is this enough to justify this expense? Most definitely not!

Correct decisions:

The two colleagues made some correct and some incorrect decisions. Let's identify the correct ones first:

- If you are going to open an office, **use the most modern office technology**. This means computers, rather than paper.
- See if you can **turn the entire practice digital**, not just the records.
- **Consult** with other docs before you chose a vendor.

Incorrect decisions:

The most important mistake they made was not looking to see if the same could have been accomplished for less money. No doubt the expensive software does a good job. At that price, it better! No doubt a Rolls-Royce is a good car. But should you rush and buy one too? With borrowed money? Absolutely not. Buy a Toyota instead!

- **A word processor and a scanner** would have computerized their medical records just as effectively. The word processor would be used for creating generic notes and writing their own notes. The scanner for scanning all incoming paper, such as radiology reports, labs and letters from other docs.
- **Cheap billing software** would have computerized their billings and scheduling.
- They did not think what would happen if the **software vendor goes out of business**. Remember, we are in the early days of office software. A lot of today's vendors will not be around tomorrow. If their vendor disappears, they will have to buy a new package. Will the new software read the files created by the old one? If not,

they are toast!

- **They forgot about cost control**. There are many cool things you can buy that work well, such as Rolls-Royce autos. But what about the price? My definition of a big expense is anything over $ 20! I would have counseled them to pinch their dollars at this time. If their practice takes off and they find themselves swimming in money, they could buy a Rolls-Royce anytime later.

Chapter 13: CLOUDS ON THE HORIZON

Motto: If you stick your head in the sand today, tomorrow you will grit your teeth.

When you embark on the journey to your own private practice, consider yourself lucky. Assuming you do your homework and learn all you need to learn, this can be a rewarding experience. Doctors have a unique freedom, which is precisely the freedom of opening their own shops <u>and</u> keeping them open for as long as they want. At the present time, a private practitioner can be reasonably assured his office will feed him and feed him well. The income of a doctor in private practice will be in 90th percentile. That is a comforting thought. Of course, if you fail to follow the principles of good business you can fall to great depths. Many do! But in my view they have only themselves to blame. Barring such self-inflicted disasters, what can possibly happen to ruin your day?

Too many doctors?

At this time, there are just about enough doctors. Of course, there are geographic areas where there are not enough (like the proverbial sticks!) and others where there are too many (like most metro areas). But overall, a medical student entering his first year today can look forward to a long and satisfying career. But what if, for some reason or another, the nation produces too many doctors? This is not an imaginary threat. For a while, in the early 80s it looked like we had too many docs. I don't know what happened exactly, and I'm not sure anybody knows, but the problem went away. I trust in market forces: if a career in medicine becomes less attractive, fewer students will enter medical school, thereby restoring equilibrium between demand and supply. For now I would not worry about it, but what if it really happens? Can you prepare? Of course you can:

- Always live within your means, don't carry debt (pay off that house!) and save as much money as you can. That way, if you should find yourself crowded by competition, you can smile and say: "What, me worry? I've saved enough. I don't need to chase every dollar".
- Always watch your costs. From the moment you open your office, cost control becomes your middle name: you are now Joe Cost Control Shmoe, MD. Have realistic goals. As a doc you will not

make millions, but you can live well enough. If you have to tighten the belt, remember, you are still doing better than most working stiffs.

The uninsured

In my view this is the biggest threat to all private practitioners today. You hear a lot about the 40 million people, who are uninsured, a number that has been rising and is predicted to continue to rise. I never understood whether these 40 million are the same people from year to year, or whether they are different people caught without insurance at different points in their lives. The politicians who run for office promising universal coverage never say (Hillary Clinton!). It makes all the difference. If this is a crowd that changes all the time, I would not worry much about them. They could very well be people that are temporarily unemployed, or who choose not to buy insurance, or who knows. But if this is a constant group of individuals, eventually they will make noise. And what they will shout for is Government intervention (see below).

The Government takes over

If Uncle Sam takes over health care, if all docs become civil servants, all bets are off. Sorry, pal, but I don't have any words of wisdom for such an eventuality. At best, a doctor would still be allowed to see private patients on the side, for example in the evening, after finishing with his Government job. At worst, all docs become Government employees with all associated consequences. Income will be down, but so will the workload. Have you every seen a Government worker bust his ass? Neither have I! However, the patients will suffer the most: think waiting lines for all procedures. Ah, also, malpractice will no longer be an issue. Good luck suing Uncle Sam!

The US does not have a health care (delivery) system

Whenever politicians tell us our health care system is the best in the world, I start laughing. I laugh even harder when I hear it needs to be reformed. Hilary Clinton comes to mind again! What was that gal talking about? **The US does not have a health care (delivery) system!** It has a hodgepodge of solutions applied unevenly to various populations. We have Medicare, arguably the only true fee-for-service insurance, but it only covers the seniors, dialysis and disabilities. We have the employer sponsored group insurance, which only covers the employed (obviously!). We have COBRA, which covers the formerly, but not yet again employed, who can afford the premiums. Finally, we have individual insurance. This one is particularly praiseworthy, since it strives to make a profit by excluding the sick, i.e., precisely those who need health insurance the most (see below). What is all this talk about "reforming the system"? **There is no system to reform. A system would have to be created first!** Sorry Lady Hillary, maybe you get to reform something in your next life-time!

What if the US decides (as a nation) to implement a uniform health care delivery system? This could very well happen. What would be the position of a private practitioner in the new system? Your guess is as good as mine!

Health insurance as a "for profit" business

This is a very big cloud, in my opinion. Wherever you look, all industrialized countries have non-profit health care delivery systems. In my opinion, health insurance is by definition non-profit. I think most health insurance executives worry very much that the nation will demand of them that they do what they were supposed to do all along: namely insure all comers, irrespective of their health status. Good-bye stock options! Why is this a cloud on the doctor's horizon? Should new laws be passed that would required health insurances to take all comers and therefore to become non-profit, reimbursement to doctors would certainly change. Will it go up, or down? Who knows!

You get wiped-out by a malpractice suit

At this time, I don't have any words of wisdom on this. It is a danger that we all live with day-to-day. It can happen to all of us anytime. Let's all wish that salaried jobs will always be there. VA Hospital, here I come...

Chapter 14: BUYING A PRACTICE

Motto: If you turn off the light fast enough, you can see the darkness.

Buying a practice is complicated business, even for experienced docs. You need a consultant to hold your hand, someone who has done practice valuations and sales before. Many times before. You also need a good lawyer to dissect the sale contract. There are several books on how to buy a practice. You need to read them. In this chapter I am giving you my personal perspective and emphasis. But, please, don't just read this chapter and then go buy a practice. You still need to read books and hire a consultant cum lawyer as an appendage.

PEARL OF WISDOM

It is better to buy a practice than to start one with no patients. There is a trend I noticed: Seeing that salaried jobs are fewer than they used to be, some residents want to begin their careers by opening their own shops. The big question for these doctors is **"Where are the patients?"**. Where are the clients that are going to pay your rent, your lunch and your kids' clothes? The lack of clients is a problem that many simply refuse to acknowledge. They do not understand that it takes many years to take a practice from zero patients to full. What are they going to live on during this time? Borrowed money? I think doctors who want to start their careers by opening their own shops are making a mistake. I said so elsewhere in this book. Briefly, the reasons are lack of money, experience and time. But **if you absolutely have to have your own practice from day one of your career, BUY ONE!** The obvious advantage is you are buying the patients. The disadvantage is that buying a practice is not for beginners, in my opinion. It requires a dose of life experience. But if you absolutely have to go with your head through the wall, pick a softer wall. Meaning you should buy an established practice, full of patients, rather than open a new one with no patients.

Let's talk about a concrete example. Let's say you want to practice in a neighborhood that is choke-full with doctors. There are plenty of places like that, for example any posh part of any metro area. If you open a new practice in such an area, you will likely have an empty waiting room. The way to "break into" such a neighborhood is by acquiring the practice of a retiring doc. Before we go into the details, let's establish some assumptions:

- **You really, really, really want to establish yourself in such an area.** Look at it this way: the rent in all posh neighborhoods will be much higher than in "regular" ones. But will the insurance reimbursement also be higher? In other words, will the higher operating expenses be compensated by higher income? I can tell you that in Phoenix the reimbursement is the same in all neighborhoods! Of course, there are neighborhoods where you will see predominantly Medicaid patients. Their reimbursement will likely be lower than average. But careful! Such generalizations are often made in absence of any supporting data. It depends on your specialty. Medicaid reimbursement may be lower for some specialties (compared with average) and higher for others! Do your research very carefully before you rush to conclusions. Remember, cost control is a very important aspect of all business activity. If you lock-in high operating costs by renting in an expensive area, you may find yourself out of business sooner than you planned. There are good reasons for opening an office in a posh area: your patients will likely be more "scrubbed" than elsewhere and they may also be willing to pay cash every once in a while.
- **You have a specialty that is heavily dependent on the buying power of the population you serve.** Read "plastic surgeon" or indeed any other doctor, who is going to do a lot of cosmetic procedures. Patients who have the cash to siliconize their bodies probably live in the more expensive zip codes. They will not choose a doctor in the low-rent part of town. If that is your target population, you have no choice but to learn to live with high operating costs.

There are other reasons for wanting to buy a practice, rather than opening a new one; for example, you did your residency in Los Angeles, but you are from Denver and you want to go back and practice in the community where you grew up. Of course, you can work for a group in Denver for a few years, build-up a following among patients, then leave the group and take your patients with you to your own shop. But you can skip the salaried period altogether by simply buying a practice. There are good reasons for wanting to "go home" to practice: you are familiar with the geography, you have family and social contacts.

The same reasoning applies to rural areas. Let's say you are a generalist and want to practice in Boondocks, New Mexico, a community with only a hand-full of people. Let us further assume that there is a family practitioner in Boondocks already. You cannot open a second new practice because the community is too small to support two docs. The way to do it is by purchasing the practice of the only doc in town. Assuming, of course, he is ready to retire!

What is worth paying for ?

Let's cut to the core of the issue: when you buy a practice, **the only thing worth money is the old doc's willingness to introduce you to his patients** as a worthy successor! The rest is not worth very much, in my opinion. Again, what you really want to buy are the patients! That is precisely how you should think of it, **you are buying the patients!** The patients are your source of income. They are worth money, not the old furniture you're going to sit on. Here are some important issues to watch for:

- **The old doc must really retire and "disappear".** Perhaps he just wants to make some money from the sale of the practice, only to open another one of his own for part-time work. You must never agree to that! Your sale contract must state that the old doc cannot open another shop in that community. You must have a very strong non-compete clause in the contract. The old guy really needs to go. Retire to Florida, die, go to a nursing home, whatever. As long as he is completely removed as a potential competitor. However, in my view he must truly leave the community. You don't want him as a competitor, but you don't want him hanging around commenting on your style of practice either: "These young punks just don't know how to use a stethoscope any more!"
- **The old doc must take the time to introduce you to his patients.** This takes a lot of time and a lot of effort. It must be done in good faith to work. In fact, it must be done in exceptionally good faith. Ideally, he should let you work alongside him for a few months and slowly hand over to you. This is extraordinarily difficult to accomplish. It is much more likely that you will have discord rather than agreement.
- **If the old doc torpedoes you in any way, you're toast!** This can be done in obvious or subtle ways. Direct comments to patients can damage your prospects of a successful take-over. Comments such as "I regret that I am too old to continue working. When I look at the docs the schools produce these days...", or "I have to sell the practice, but I'm not sure what to think of my successor" will likely chase the patients away. But he does not have to be so direct. Subtle measures work just as well. For example, he could tell a key employee to leave.
- **Make sure you can take over his insurance contracts.** Remember, even if the old doc acts in good faith, the insurances may not. You must sign contracts with all of them before you hand over money to the retiring doc. No contracts, no patients, no matter how much the old doc recommended you to his patients.
- **If the old doc was in business for a long time, beware of set ways!**

The patients know him and he knows them. There is a bond. Are they likely to bond with you, or are they going to bolt instead of bond? The same applies to personnel. Very likely you are going to make changes. Will the staff embrace them, or will they leave?

- **Will the staff sabotage you?** As soon as you take over, you will find surprises. Things you could not have possibly known about. For example, the old doc slept with the receptionist. Yes, it was discreet, but everybody knew it anyway. Therefore, the receptionist was off-limits to any disciplinary measures and to any real performance appraisals from the manager. How are you going to deal with a member of the staff who is used to preferential treatment? The answer is, of course, you're not! You are going to lay off the receptionist. But guess what? Maybe the receptionist was very popular with patients and once gone, the receptionist is free to fire poison darts at you! Think negative comments to patients and so on.

What is worth some money, but not as much as you think

It goes without saying that you should look at every item in the practice you are buying and ask yourself if you want to keep it. It is like being in a store for used office equipment. Here are some thoughts:

- **The paper charts.** Very likely the old doc was not computerized. You must have all his charts. They are certainly worth paying for. Even if his notes are of the "patient alive, drugs renewed" kind. You have no choice but to purchase those.
- **The furniture.** Take it, even if it is not to your taste. Patients are used to that particular ambiance. It is ok to make changes, but do so slowly. I would start with your room rather than the waiting room.
- **Medical equipment and supplies.** Take it! Used is much cheaper than new.
- **Computers.** If the practice has a computer system, take it over no matter how antiquated. Computer systems are notoriously difficult to replace. Glitches are very common. How many times have you heard "We are open for business, but we cannot do anything, because we have a new computer system and it is not working as we hoped for"? If the antiquated computer system works, keep it!
- **Paper and pencils.** Ordinary office supplies that is. Keep them but insist on getting them free, or at a very deep discount. Here you are in the driver's seat: no departing doc is going to take his old photocopier and speaker phone with him. He will likely agree to a discount.

The staff

Again, you would be foolish not to keep them. They are in fact your only effective link with the patients for a long time to come. They know the patients already and the patients know them. It is best to keep the staff and use them to help you connect with the patients. Let's say you have a patient whom the old doc has furnished with narcotics for many years. You think it needs to be stopped and tell the patient this is the last prescription. The patient will be very irritated, to say the least. This is where a good nurse would help you a lot by smoothing the waters: "Yes. Mr. Soandso I don't think the new doc will renew your morphine, but he is a good doc and cares for you very much. If you are willing to work with him, he will find something acceptable". In fact, in the beginning you are pretty much at the mercy of the staff. You must court them and make them accept you. At least until you are up and running. You will make (many) changes in staff, eventually. But in the beginning, tread lightly!

A FINAL WORD

A FINAL PEARL OF WISDOM

Starting a medical practice is a bewildering experience, if you have never done it before. When I started, I went to a friend of mine, who had been in private practice for several years. I spent time in his office trying to learn the ropes. One day, his office manager tried to teach me how to do payroll. He said payroll was the easiest thing to do. However, 10 minutes into the presentation I had already lost track of what was going on and was feeling like the floor had fallen out from under me. My teacher was saying something like "You need to get an employer ID number from the Feds, another one from the state, the state tax office and the state employment office, you need to pay payroll taxes on the first $7,000 of each one of your employees, you need to keep track of worked hours, sick time, vacation time, enter the appropriate number of hours in your accounting software, buy workers' compensation insurance..." You get the picture. If this is the easiest thing to do, what is the most complex?

This book deals with the fundamental knowledge needed to open and run a practice. However, not all you need to know can be learned from books. Very likely you will need on-site help. Someone needs to sit down with you and show you how it's done. If you don't master it the first time around, don't despair. When it comes to new knowledge, especially bone-dry knowledge, like doing payroll, repetition is the key. Initially, I felt like I'll never understand payroll. Never, ever! Yet now I do payroll in five minutes if I'm slow.

Opening a medical practice without expert help is a mistake. My advice is to ask a consultant to hold your hand in the beginning. I did too. Now I switched roles and I make a living helping other doctors. Many docs are reluctant to pay a consultant to teach them. They think it is an expense best avoided. After all, cost control is important. However, my experience shows it is money well spent. It is important to establish a working relationship with a practice management consultant early in your career. That way, if you get stuck, you can ask for help. "I'm trying to do payroll, but the software just printed a paycheck for $ 1,000,000 for my receptionist. Can you come over and help me out?"

If you think this book was helpful, but you still have questions, please do not hesitate to call me. I can be reached at my consulting company, as noted below.

All comments, questions and profanities can be e-mailed from the website. And if you are looking for a consultant for your practice, I have a bottomless bag of good advice at a very reasonable price!

Chris Rainer, MD, MPH
Sunbelt International Consulting, LLC
A comprehensive practice management consulting company
www.sunbeltinternationalconsulting.com

Bibiliography

The small-business library

On LLCs:

-**Form Your Own Limited Liability Company** by Anthony Mancuso.
Publisher: Nolo (this is a publisher of many business related and legal advice books)
ISBN: 0-87337-797-4

This is a "must read" for all those who are opening a practice. The LLC form of doing business is an obvious and very practical way of going into private practice. This book explains all you need to know. Don't be scared because of the books' size: half of it is taken up by references to the laws in all 50 states.

On management techniques:

-**The Supervisor's Book of Lists** by George T. Fuller
Publisher: Prentice Hall ISBN: 0-13-122771-8

By looking at these lists, you gather insight into the process of management itself. It is more than just a book on listing things and prioritizing, because it conveys basic knowledge too.

-**Managing for dummies** by Bob Nelson & Peter Economy
Publisher: IDG books (the "for dummies" series of books)
ISBN:1-56884-858-7

This is a very good 101 course in management. Since you are not looking at being the next CEO of Megamedicine, Inc., this is all you need to manage your practice in general and your employees in particular.

On negotiating, which comes in handy when you negotiate with health insurances:

-**Negotiating for Dummies** by Michael C. Donaldson & Mimi Donaldson
Publisher: Hungry Minds (also from the "for dummies" series)
ISBN: 1-56884-867-6

Negotiating is a learned "art". Few are born with all the knowledge needed to get what you want out of a business encounter. Easy to read and well organized.

On financial advice:

-Making the Most of Your Money by Jane Bryant Quinn
Publisher: Simon & Schuster ISBN: 0-671-65952-9

In my view, the only book you need on financial stuff. If you only read this book and no other, you would not have missed anything essential. If covers the whole gamut of issues, from checking accounts, homeowner's insurance, description of financial instruments to retirement planning strategies. This author did her homework very thoroughly. I read it cover-to-cover, but I also use it often as a reference work.

-The Basics of Investing by Benton E. Gup
Publisher: Wiley & Sons ISBN: 0-471-54853-7

This is the academic equivalent of Quinn's book. I read this one from cover to cover too. Very likely, you would need to go to a college book store to find this book.

On practice management

-Starting a Medical Practice by Jeffrey P. Daigrepont, AMA press, ISBN 1-57947-296-6. I like the countdown to opening day.

-The Business of Medical Practice. Profit maximizing skills for savvy doctors by David Edward Marcinko (Editor), Springer Publishing Company ISBN 0-8261-1311-7. This is a rather pretentious book that seems to delve in the academic realm and comes short on practical advice.

-How to Join, Buy or Merge a Physician's Practice by Yvonne Mart Fox and Brett A. Levine, Mosby, ISBN 0-8151-2878-9. A good guide, easy to read with enough practical suggestions to make it worth reading.

On coding

Every year, you must order the new Medicare reimbursement, CPT and ICD books:

Current Procedural Terminology, which is a book of codes that assigns a 5 digit number to everything you can possibly do to a patient, from an office visit to a brain transplant. Published by the American Medical Association, costs ~$60, order at 800/621-8335

International Classification of Diseases, a book that assigns a number to every disease known to mankind. I get mine from Practice Management Information Corporation (PMIC) for ~$55. Contact www.pmiconline.com or 800/med-shop, or 4727 Wilshire Blvd #300 Los Angeles, CA 90010

Medicare Part B Provider Disclosure Report (for the state where you practice), which has all Medicare reimbursement information for Arizona. Costs ~$10. Call 877/908-8431, or contact Medicare Service Center 4305 13th Avenue Fargo, ND 58103-3373. If you are already registered with Medicare, you'll get this mailed to you each year. You can also look it up at the website of your Medicare carrier, for example noridianmedicare.com.

Things to read regularly

- www.amednews.com. This is the weekly AMA newspaper. I read it every week. It is a very good source of knowledge of a host of issues concerning the practicing doc. For example, when HIPAA became an issue, this publication guided me to all I needed to implement the new mandates.
- www.aafp.org. A good website to visit for any doc, not just family practitioners. Their office management section is super!

For books that are out of print

Try Harvest Booksearch: 800/563-1222 or 215/619-0697 Fax: 215/619-0308 e-mail: search@harvestbooks.com Harvest Book Company, LLC 260 New York Drive # B, Fort Washington, PA 19034

This company may very well find the book that everybody else cannot locate.

Index

W

Y

About The Author

Dr. Rainer studied medicine in Germany and London and epidemiology at UCLA. He completed his internal medicine residency at Good Samaritan Hospital in Phoenix. After practicing internal medicine for a number of years, he is now managing his wife's surgery practice, consulting on practice management issues and teaching practice management to residents.

His consulting company is called Sunbelt International Consulting, and the website is:
www.sunbeltinternationalconsulting.com.

NOTES

NOTES